Chapter 1

'More toilet paper needed in the first-floor ladies'.'

Mrs White's voice crackled in Alice's earpiece, the broad Devonshire accent instantly recognisable.

Alice reached for the two-way radio clipped to her lapel and waited until a pair of grey-haired visitors had walked past, smiling amiably. She smiled politely back at them before answering. 'Okay, Mrs White, I'll get somebody onto it right away.'

'Thanking you, my lovely.'

Alice spotted young Mary just emerging from the library, gave her a little wave to attract her attention and dispatched her to the store to find and deliver fresh supplies. As they all knew well, if an army marches on its stomach, a stately home open to the public marches on gallons of tea, tasty cakes and well-maintained toilets.

Seconds later, her earpiece crackled again. This time it was a different voice. 'Alice, can you spare me five minutes? There's somebody here who wants to talk to you.' It was Marjorie, the manager, and she sounded a bit strange, a bit strained.

'Yes, of course, Marjorie, I'll be right there. I just need to check that the computer problem on the front desk has been sorted first.'

There were twenty-eight steps up to the first floor and Alice's knee was aching by the time she got up to the broad landing. Some days she felt little or no pain but today was cool and damp outside and it somehow got into her bones. Marjorie's office on the first floor had once been the dressing room belonging to a succession of Fitzgerald-Chagleigh wives, back in the days when ladies of high standing needed entire rooms to house their extensive collections of clothes, not to mention several pairs of hands to assist with lacing them into their corsets and helping them into their extravagant frocks and gowns. Now the clothes had disappeared – some to Exeter Museum and some of them on display elsewhere in the manor house – corsets had gone out of fashion, and helping hands were in short supply as recession began to bite.

Nowadays the room contained little more than a desk and a pair of upright upholstered chairs which had originally been in a corner of the ladies' parlour on the ground floor. On the walls were a blown-up aerial photo of the Fitzgerald-Chagleigh estate, a floor plan of the house showing all thirty-three rooms and, rather unsettlingly, four of the original mirrors left over from the room's former purpose, in which Alice could see her own reflection from two different angles as she approached the serious-looking lady already sitting in front of Marjorie's desk. Alice had a sinking feeling that she knew who this was.

She wasn't wrong.

'Alice, come and sit down. This is Helen from the HR department in London.' There was something different in the house manager's voice today – sympathy, maybe –

Change of Heart

T.A. Williams lives in Devon with his Italian wife. He was born in England of a Scottish mother and Welsh father. After a degree in modern languages at Nottingham University, he lived and worked in Switzerland, France and Italy, before returning to run one of the best-known language schools in the UK. He's taught Arab princes, Brazilian beauty queens and Italian billionaires. He speaks a number of languages and has travelled extensively. He has eaten snake, still-alive fish, and alligator. A Spanish dog, a Russian bug and a Korean parasite have done their best to eat him in return. His hobby is long-distance cycling, but his passion is writing.

Also by T.A. Williams

Chasing Shadows
Dreaming of Venice
Dreaming of Florence
Dreaming of St-Tropez
Dreaming of Christmas
Dreaming of Tuscany
Dreaming of Rome
Dreaming of Verona
Dreaming of Italy

Escape to Tuscany

Under a Siena Sun
Second Chances in Chianti
Secrets on the Italian Island

Love from Italy

A Little Piece of Paradise
An Escape to Remember
A Chance in a Million

Beneath Italian Skies

Never Too Late
Change of Heart

T.A. WILLIAMS

Change of heart

10 CANELO

First published in the United Kingdom in 2023 by

Canelo
Unit 9, 5th Floor
Cargo Works, 1–2 Hatfields
London SE1 9PG
United Kingdom

A CIP catalogue record for this book is available from the British Library.

Print ISBN 978 1 80436 243 3
Ebook ISBN 978 1 80436 242 6

This book is a work of fiction. Names, characters, businesses, organizations, places and events are either the product of the author's imagination or are used fictitiously. Any resemblance to actual persons, living or dead, events or locales is entirely coincidental.

Cover design by Rose Cooper

Cover images © iStock

Look for more great books at www.canelo.co

Printed and bound in Great Britain by Clays Ltd, Elcograf S.p.A.

I

To Mariangela, Christina and Iris with love.

and this only added to Alice's feeling of impending doom. 'She's been telling me about a number of changes coming down the line that are going to affect all of us.'

Helen from the HR department probably wasn't more than five or six years older than Alice herself – maybe in her mid-thirties – and she was looking uncomfortable. As Alice spied the expression on the woman's face, that same sensation of discomfort – or more – settled on her as well, and not just because of her aching knee. This didn't look like it was going to be good news. There had been rumours of funding cuts and maybe even redundancies for some weeks now, but she had been hoping for the best. She had been doing this job for almost four years since coming back from Italy, and had worked her way up to her current position of assistant manager, hoping to make a real career of it and rise to the rank of house manager or even higher. To see that go up in flames would be a bitter blow.

Automatically, she took Helen's proffered hand and shook it, her mind already turning over what might be to come. Her fears were immediately confirmed by what the visitor from London said next.

'Good morning, Alice, I'm afraid I bring some not very welcome news.'

As she listened, Alice's heart sank like a stone. Helen cleared her throat and continued in a gentle, consolatory tone that did nothing to stem Alice's rising sense of disappointment and dismay.

'As I've just been telling Marjorie, government funding has been cut back, and our budget for the coming year has had to be slashed accordingly. I'm afraid the result is that we're all going to have to tighten our belts.' Seeing the expression on Alice's face, she was quick to offer reassurance – up to a point. 'Now I don't want you to worry too much, but the problem we have is that we need to scale down the staffing here and in our other properties across the country and increase reliance on volunteers. To that end, I'm afraid the position of assistant manager will cease to exist. Marjorie thinks very highly of you, and we agree that we would like to keep you on, but I'm afraid it will have to be in a less senior role.' She allowed a more positive note to enter her voice, but Alice noticed that she didn't have the nerve to look either of them in the eye. 'I know it's not what you wanted to hear, but it's not as though you're being made redundant.'

'When you say a less senior role, what exactly does that mean?' Alice spotted her own face reflected in the big mirror on the office wall and had a sudden vision of herself sitting at the Jobcentre, cap in hand. 'Are you saying I would have to go back to just being an ordinary employee again?'

Helen nodded, and Marjorie supplied the coup de grâce. 'I'm afraid you'll have to drop a paygrade, Alice, but at least you would still be working here at the manor.'

As Helen went on to outline the detail of the new position being offered – essentially exactly what Alice had started out doing four years ago – and the corresponding drop in pay, Alice's heart sank even more. Apart from shattering her career hopes, this would cause her major financial complications. She was only just managing the mortgage payments on her tiny cottage out of her current salary. If this was cut, she would probably lose her house. Her reflection in the mirror revealed an expression of bitter disappointment on her face, and as soon as she was able to escape from the office, she hurried out of the room, telling them she would need to think about what she was going to do.

She went straight down the stairs, walking blindly through the lobby without even acknowledging Polly or Jake behind the reception desk, and headed out of the front door. She could feel herself limping heavily but she didn't stop to fetch her stick. She had far more important concerns on her mind. She wandered out into the ornate Italianate garden, created by Capability Brown two hundred and fifty years earlier. Today the gorgeous display of spring flowers barely registered with her as she walked aimlessly along the gravel paths, past the ornate fountain with its delicately carved nymphs and dolphins, oblivious to the light April drizzle on her head and shoulders. It was only when she reached the stable block that she was forced to return her attention to her surroundings as a familiar voice shook her out of her stupor.

'Good afternoon, Alice, you look as if you've seen a ghost. Don't tell me the Mad Marquis has been making his presence felt again.'

Alice blinked a couple of times and looked up into the face of her friend. 'Hi there, Fenella, I'm afraid I was miles away. No, no ghosts; just bitter reality I'm afraid.'

'You look as though you could do with a good hot cup of tea, or maybe a glass of something stronger. Why don't you come over to the house and tell me what the problem is? I've just come back from my afternoon ride, and I could do with a sit down and a chance to dry out.'

Lord and Lady Fitzgerald-Chagleigh lived in the Dower House. Crippling death duties fifty years earlier had forced Ronald's parents to gift the manor house and the estate to National Heritage, and all the family were left with now was the admittedly magnificent sixteenth-century stone house with its large garden and the shared use of the old stables for Fenella's horses. Alice had struck up a close friendship with Lady Fitzgerald-Chagleigh since starting to work here at the manor, even though her ladyship was over twice Alice's age and from a totally different family background. She was a very dynamic woman and the two of them often went riding together when Alice was able to take time off.

'Thanks, Fenella, but I don't think I'd be very good company today.'

'Let me be the judge of that. Come on, let's go and have a cuppa.'

Alice allowed herself to be led out of the wooden gate at the far end of the gardens, ignoring the *PRIVATE PROPERTY, NO ENTRY* sign, and onto the gravel path alongside the magnificent expanse of lawn in front of the Dower House. If Fenella noticed her more pronounced limp today, she didn't comment. That was something else that Alice liked about her: she didn't go in for a lot of fuss. Loud yapping from inside the house indicated that Fenella's poodle, Gladys, must have heard the squeaky gate and was keen to welcome her mistress home. The front door opened before they got there, and the excited dog came rushing out, followed by Ronald, Lord F-C himself. He gave his wife a small smile and gave Alice a broader one.

'Hello, Alice. How lovely to see you. Come inside before you get soaked.'

Alice managed to muster a smile in return and followed Fenella into the house, the dog still yapping at their heels. Five minutes later she was sitting in the charming lounge nursing a sore leg and a mug of hot tea, while Fenella, freshly changed into a sensible tweed skirt, took a seat opposite her and then leant forward, elbows on her knees.

'Right, go on then, tell me what the problem is. I'm sure we can solve it.' As usual, there was a friendly smile on her ladyship's face.

Alice shook her head ruefully. 'I'm afraid that might not be possible. This is out of my hands, and even yours.' She went on to outline what she had just been told in Marjorie's office and read sympathy on the faces of her host and hostess. When she got to the end of her tale of woe, she sat back and sipped her tea while the little dog stood up on its hindlegs and did its best to climb onto her lap. Fenella took her time before replying.

'Well, one thing's for sure: you can't take a downward step. That would be just too terribly depressing and I'm sure you wouldn't want to take a pay cut. Gladys, come here! Leave Alice alone.'

Alice nodded in agreement. 'It would be awfully depressing, but what choice do I have? At least, what choice do I have if I want to stay in the same sort of job? Stately homes open to the public aren't that common around here, and I imagine they'll all be in the same position with these government cuts.'

'Then you have a simple binary choice.' Fenella had always been a pragmatic sort of person. 'Assuming you're not prepared to take a pay cut and demotion – and you're quite right not to want to take such a backward step – then as I see it you either need to look for a job in the

7

same sector elsewhere or find a completely different job around here.'

'This part of England isn't exactly overflowing with job opportunities. I might be able to find something on a temporary basis over the summer, looking after holiday lets or working in a pub or something similar – assuming it didn't mean having to be on my feet all the time – but as soon as the autumn comes, I know I'd be out of work again. Besides, those jobs probably won't pay any more than National Heritage are offering me.'

'Then we're just going to need to cast our net wider, aren't we?' Alice was touched to hear her friend use the pronoun 'we', but she knew her chances of finding something suitable weren't great.

'Definitely sounds to me as though you should look further afield.' Ronald had been standing by the piano, making no comment up till now, and Alice turned her head towards him as he continued. 'If the British government are cutting back, maybe other countries aren't in such dire economic straits. You speak Italian, don't you?' Alice nodded and he prodded a bit further. 'How well do you speak it? I know a few people over there. I could ask around and see if there's anything going.'

'That's very sweet of you. I actually speak Italian pretty well, but I haven't been back in four years, and I'm not sure how I'd feel about trying again. I spent five years living and working there after university but it never led to anything, and I'd already decided I needed to look for something more satisfying and more permanent back here in the UK when the accident happened. You both know the story.'

Fenella caught her eye and nodded. The story of Alice's crushed leg and the ensuing months of rehab that had caused her to give up her job and return to the UK was well known to her. Alice buried her face in her mug of tea while Ronald carried on.

'You never know, things may have changed over there. You won't know unless you try, will you? Whereabouts in Italy were you? Might there be something in that area? Old friends you could contact?'

Alice shook her head again. 'Not really. I was up in the very north of Italy, high in the Dolomites, but there were precious few opportunities in the heritage business up there. I've still got friends up there, but about the only guaranteed vacancies are as ski instructors or mountain guides, and there's no way I could even think of something like that now. I was lucky to find the job I did, but the accident put paid to it.'

'What were you doing over there?'

'The same sort of thing as I do here. I was working in a lovely old former monastery near Cortina d'Ampezzo – initially as a guide and then I got promoted to back-office work, dealing with the local authorities and all that sort of thing. For a while, I genuinely thought it might lead to something bigger and better but, if anything, they were even more strapped for cash then we are over here. No, I doubt there's much point in thinking about Italy again.'

'But wouldn't they take you back, you know, temporarily while you look around for something else?'

The answer to that, Alice felt sure, was yes. Before she had left, the director up there had told her there would always be a job for her if she wanted to come back, but he and she had both known that it would never lead anywhere. Besides, although she had never told anybody apart from her mum, there was another reason why she had no desire to return to the Dolomites, and his name was Maurizio. She had been going out with him for almost a year when the accident happened, but the moment he realised that she was never going to be the same again, he dropped her like a hot cake. After her return to the UK she had never heard from him again; the idea of running into him was distasteful and she knew it would bring back a host of bad memories. She shook her head regretfully but left Maurizio out of it.

'I expect I could get my old job back, but then I'd just find myself stuck in the same old rut again. That's why I thought this job here at the manor was the opportunity I needed, but now I feel as if the rug's been pulled from under my feet.'

Fenella reached out with her free hand and gave Alice's good knee a supportive tap. 'Try not to let it get you down, Alice. We'll spread the word and I'm sure we'll find something for you. Leave it to us.'

Chapter 2

Lord and Lady Fitzgerald-Chagleigh were as good as their word. Barely four days after her fateful meeting with the HR lady, Alice got a text message from Fenella.

> We have news. Can you drop in for a drink
> on your way home tonight?

Intrigued, Alice replied immediately and duly went across to the Dower House at six o'clock. As usual, she was greeted with a barrage of excited yapping from the poodle and a warm welcome from the friendly couple who led her through to the lounge. A glass of amontillado was thrust into her hand, and she sat down to hear what they had to say.

'We think we might have found exactly the right thing for you, Alice.' Fenella was looking and sounding very bubbly. 'Ronald was speaking to one of his friends in London who knows somebody in Milan who knows somebody in Parma, and it looks like there's a vacancy for a person with exactly your qualifications and experience.' She held up her hands to stop Alice from saying anything. 'Before you say it, Ronald's told them that you have some mobility problems and they say that wouldn't be a problem. This really does sound like too good an opportunity to miss.'

Alice nodded mutely, thinking hard, trying to remember where Parma was. She knew it was somewhere in central or northern Italy, but she wasn't completely sure. Ronald must have noted her uncertainty and he explained.

'I had to look it up on the map to see exactly where it is. Parma's in northern Italy, near Modena, just above Bologna and Florence. Of course, the name was immediately familiar because of Parma ham and Parmesan cheese, but I wasn't sure where it was. I've been reading up on it and it sounds like a lovely city, and that whole area looks very historic and peppered with castles and fortresses. Mind you, that's the region where Ferrari and Lamborghini have their factories so it's potentially a rich industrial area too. The place in question is about thirty kilometres south-west of Parma, up in the hills at an altitude of about four or five hundred meters. The castle itself dates back to the thirteen hundreds, so that makes it seven hundred years old. That's even older than this place.' He sounded impressed.

'The castle?'

Alice saw him consult his iPad. 'It belongs to a family called Varaldo. Apparently they're descendants of one of the big players in Italian history, the Malaspina family, who built the original castle. My friend Cyril's friend in Milan tells me that the Varaldo family have decided to open the castle to the public for the very first time, and they need somebody with experience, to organise that for them and then stay on to run the place. With your degree in estate management and your experience in Italy and over here, we think you'd be perfect.'

Alice took a cautious sip of sherry. She had never really been a great fan of the drink, but she knew by now that Fitzgerald-Chagleigh family tradition decreed that they had to dole out glasses of it to all visitors old enough to wear long trousers. It was a bit too sweet for her taste, but quite drinkable, and this delaying tactic gave her time to think. On the face of it, the job they were proposing sounded like a gift from the gods – especially if they really didn't mind that she wasn't as mobile as she used to be. The trouble was that it would be a major step to take and one fraught with uncertainties. Still, as much for the sake of these two kind people as anything else, she did her best to give it serious consideration.

A medieval castle sounded amazing, although whether or not it would lend itself to being opened to the public would depend very much on its condition. While her knowledge of Italian health and safety regulations was four years old now, Alice was reasonably sure nothing much would have changed. Just like here in the UK, no chances should be taken. If any part of the building looked like it was going to collapse on top of visitors, or if any place or object presented a hazard, there would be no way the owners would be able to get permission or, more crucially, obtain the all-important accident and injury insurance to allow them to proceed. Before she could query further, it appeared that Ronald had been thinking along the same lines. He picked up his iPad again, scrolled through and handed it across to her.

'Here it is. See what you think. Considering how old it is, it looks in pretty good condition.'

Alice put down her glass and studied the photo on the screen. This showed a very beautiful and quite obviously ancient fortress, complete with crenelated battlements, towers, a moat and arrow slit windows on the lower levels. The castle was situated on a little rise, partway up a bigger hill, surrounded by dense woodland and occasional green fields, and with two or three red-roofed buildings dotted about amid the trees. To her trained eye, however, the castle itself didn't look totally medieval. Maybe it had been renovated more recently and, if so, that would make it a lot easier to bring it up to the standard necessary to open it to the public. The caption below it read: *Castello di Varaldo, comune di Varaldo, Emilia-Romagna.*

'Emilia-Romagna is the name of the region, and Varaldo's the name of the nearby village.' Ronald leant over and pointed to the higher hills in the background. 'It's on the north-eastern flank of the Apennines – I'm sure you know they're the mountains that form the spine of Italy – strategically positioned so as to guard what was one of the main mountain passes. According to the Internet, Varaldo was on a major trade and pilgrimage route that was used for centuries.'

Alice nodded, but barely took in what he was saying. Her attention was totally on the castle. From what she could see, the upper floors looked as if they were being lived in, so presumably the place couldn't be *too* dilapidated. The building and its surroundings were very different from the Tyrolean-style houses and rocky Alpine peaks of the Dolomites, and it could almost have been in a different country. As for the castle itself, it looked like it might be possible to transform it into a tourist attraction, but she felt sure it was going to be a considerable challenge. She handed the computer back and looked across at the two of them.

'It looks amazing but it won't be easy. Thank you so much for going to all this trouble, but I have a feeling they'll probably need somebody older and with more experience than me, probably an Italian. But I must admit it's very tempting.' She glanced across and caught Ronald's eye, mustering a little smile. 'And I suppose I really don't have a choice.'

He shot her an encouraging smile in return. 'I wouldn't worry about your age if I were you. You have the experience and the qualifications, and you speak fluent Italian. Do think seriously about it. I'm sure it would suit you down to the ground.'

Alice shot him a grateful glance. 'I *will* think about it, I promise. If I do decide to go for it, how do I contact the people?'

Ronald answered. 'Cyril – that's my pal in London – says that his friend in Milan has spoken to the people in Parma about you and they say they'd be happy to arrange an interview with you. The only thing is that he said they've already interviewed a number of applicants, so you'd better make your mind up sooner rather than later. Could you take a bit of time off and pop over to see them? Maybe even as soon as this weekend? See how comfortable you feel back in Italy again. If you don't like the place or the people, you can just say no if they offer you the job. And if they don't, you'll have had a day or two in Italy to see how you feel about the place again. But you need to make your mind up very quickly whether you want to go for it or not.'

Alice did a bit of quick thinking. The spring bank holiday in ten days' time would be busy here at the manor, but she should be able to take a couple of days off before that. She normally worked on either Saturday or Sunday, but she felt sure Marjorie would allow her to get away for a day or two this weekend, considering it was for a job interview after all, if the people over there could see her. Ronald was right. Going over to Italy for a couple of days would be fun and a way of dipping her toe in the Italian water again. If something didn't feel right, she could just say no. But if she did feel comfortable with the job and the idea of moving back to Italy, she had to admit that it sounded fascinating and tempting. She swallowed hard and made a quick decision.

Pulling out her phone, she called Marjorie to check if it might be possible to take Saturday, Sunday and maybe Monday off. For now, she didn't go into any detail, just telling her boss that there was the chance of a job. As she had thought, the answer was yes, so she was able to tell Ronald and Fenella that she would be up for the interview.

Ronald immediately made a call to his friend in London and by the time Alice had finished her sherry and politely refused a top-up, she had been given the phone number and name of the contact at the castle. Although her instincts were telling her to go off somewhere quiet and private to make the call, she could see that Ronald and Fenella were bursting with curiosity, so she pulled out her phone again and made the call. It rang half a dozen times before she heard what sounded like a young woman's voice.

'*Pronto.*'

As Alice replied, she was pleased to hear her Italian sounding reasonably fluent after four years of very little use. 'Hello, good evening, could I speak to Simonetta Varaldo, please?'

'I'm Simonetta. How can I help you?' The woman sounded friendly enough and Alice took heart.

'My name's Alice Sterling and I'm calling from England.' She went on to explain that she'd been told about the family's plans for the castle and asked if it might be possible to be considered for the position. To her surprise the reply was enthusiastic.

'We'd be delighted to meet you. Count Romano called to tell us all about you. If you give me your e-mail address, I'll send you over the information sheet we've prepared. The only thing is that we want to make a decision quickly. Is there any chance you could come over in the next few days?'

'My friends here told me you wanted to get moving as soon as possible. Today's Thursday. Would it be all right if I came to see you on Saturday or Sunday? I'll have to check flights first, of course.'

'Either day would be perfect; time to suit you. Call me back when you've made your travel plans.'

Alice thanked her and the call ended. She looked across at the other two, a feeling of excitement building inside her, alongside a hefty helping of apprehension. 'Thank you both so much. They'll see me this Saturday if I can find a flight. Who's Count Romano? Simonetta said he's already called her.'

'That'll be Cyril's friend in Milan.'

'Isn't Italy a republic nowadays? I didn't think they still had an aristocracy.'

Lord F-C smiled. 'You can't get rid of us that easily. Italy's still got princes and counts and barons all over the place, but they just don't use their titles so much. It's the same in a lot of countries these days. Trust me: the old boy network still works well in our circles.' He tapped the side of his nose conspiratorially and his smile broadened. 'I daresay I could put you in touch with a few members of the nobility in Russia if I put my mind to it.' His smile turned into a grin. 'Not so sure about the USA, though. So, the interview's set for the day after tomorrow?'

'The day after tomorrow...' Alice struggled to dominate the feeling of apprehension rising up inside her at the realisation of what lay ahead for her. 'Now all I've got to do is to find out how to get there. First things first, I need to take a look at a map of Italy.'

Chapter 3

It turned out to be remarkably easy to get to the castle. Alice got a really cheap seat on a Ryanair flight to Bologna on Saturday morning and rented an automatic Fiat at the airport. From there to Varaldo took little over an hour and a half, most of it on the very busy motorway with a never-ending series of cars zooming past her totally ignoring the speed limits, while the last twenty or thirty kilometres were on minor roads and much less stressful. These took her into the foothills of the Apennines, the mountain range that runs along the length of Italy and separates the plains of the north from the hills of Tuscany and the west coast. For the first part of the journey the terrain was almost completely flat and when she turned off the autostrada, the rounded, tree covered hills ahead of her were very different from and not as spectacular as the rugged Dolomites where she had worked before. It was all less harsh, less forbidding and more civilised. She had to admit that her first impression was very positive. So far, so good.

Now that she was on country roads and she didn't have to concentrate so hard, she allowed herself to think about what awaited her. The accident had seriously dented her confidence and the nerves that had been building up over the last couple of days returned with a rush. Would they offer her the job? Would it be a job she would want to take? More importantly, would it be a job she could do? By the look of it, it was going to be a huge challenge and she just hoped she would be up to it. Before the accident she had always been a pretty organised, pragmatic sort of person, but she knew she would have to work on this if she did take on such a potentially massive project. Was she the right woman for the job? She took a few deep breaths and reminded herself of what her father had said to her the previous day. 'There's no point in worrying about things that might happen. Worry about the things that are happening now, and the future will take care of itself.'

She hoped he was going to be proved right.

Doing her best to quell the butterflies fluttering in her stomach, she concentrated on enjoying the changing scenery and appreciating the historic buildings she passed on the way. These varied from old brick-built farmsteads where multiple families must once have lived in a self-contained community – maybe still did – to smaller, simpler dwellings and villages where plain-looking houses clustered around old churches. Compared to the Dolomites it was undramatic, and she found it remarkably soothing. Maybe it was going to be okay after all. After following a river valley for a while, she spotted a sign to the right indicating that Varaldo was only nine kilometres away. She turned onto a narrower road that started to climb more seriously through a series of tortuous bends.

As she approached her destination, she found herself debating once again what she would do if the people here offered her the job. The information she had received by e-mail was fairly brief and, as far as the salary was concerned, it just indicated a possible range, depending on age and experience. The good news was that the bottom end of the range was roughly what she had been getting as assistant manager at the manor so, hopefully, she would find herself being paid a bit more. She had no idea about property rental prices in Italy or even about the cost of living after four years, so she would have to do her sums very carefully. Her other constant concern ever since hearing about the job had been her leg. Would she be up to the job, physically? Would she be able to climb all the stairs, walk up and down the steep slopes and would the cold mountain air cause her greater discomfort? And, in the first instance, would they employ her once they knew all about her? And she owed them full disclosure.

Two or three kilometres later, she set eyes on the castle for the first time. It was easy to see why the original builders had chosen this site. The massive stone fortress was situated in the perfect spot for its owners to be able to survey and police the whole valley in both directions. Even now, it still looked imposing, and back in the Middle Ages nobody travelling up or down could have got past without the very real risk of being seen and attacked or, more probably, made to pay a toll.

Directly below the castle lay the little town of Varaldo itself. This was bigger than Alice had imagined and probably numbered several thousand people. She was pleasantly surprised to find that it boasted a selection of shops and a pretty little central piazza in front of a charming old church with a slightly wonky spire. In the square was a hotel called *La Casa Rosa*. A sign indicated that it boasted a restaurant, and tables outside on the cobbles confirmed that it also had a bar. A road led off to the right and a sign attached to the side of one of the houses indicated that this was the way to *Il Castello*.

Alice followed the road out of the town and into thick woodland. The road climbed for several hundred yards until she emerged from the trees and found herself directly in front of the castle. Seen close up, it was even more impressive and imposing, and she could well imagine that in its heyday this place would have commanded considerable respect and no small amount of fear.

She left the car by the side of the road in a muddy layby, making a mental note that before the castle could be opened to the public, they would have to provide considerable customer parking. It was noticeably colder here than it had been at Bologna airport, and she was glad of her thick woolly jumper. The good news was that the air was far drier than back in England and her knee didn't seem to have suffered after a day mostly spent sitting down. She deliberately left her stick in the car as she wanted to convince the people here that she was agile enough to do the job, but it was a considerable relief that she found walking unexpectedly easy. Hopefully this was a good omen.

She could see a light dusting of snow still on the tops of the distant hills, even though it was almost the end of April now. Entrance to the castle was across a massive wooden drawbridge over what had no doubt once been a moat. This was now little more than a deep ditch, overgrown with scrub, brambles and small trees. At the bottom of it she could also see an unpleasant assortment of rubbish. It looked as though the locals had been using the place as a dump for quite some time.

There was no sign of a doorbell or of anybody to ask, so she ignored the sign marked *PROPRIETÀ PRIVATA* and walked across the bridge and in through the arched entrance set at the base of one of the towers that punctuated the stone walls. A pair of massive wooden doors, studded with square headed nails, each the size of her fist, were opened against the walls of the gatehouse, and looking up, she was fascinated to see a rusty iron portcullis suspended high above her on equally rusty chains. This looked far from safe, so she made a point of passing through there as quickly as possible until she emerged into the open central courtyard of the castle. Here she saw a few signs of the twenty-first century.

Parked against the far end of the remarkably large open area were three cars: two nondescript small cars similar to the one she had rented, and a very muddy Land Rover. She was mildly surprised not to see something a bit more upmarket. She had assumed that anybody living in a castle would be in the high-income bracket. Of course, she told herself, this was probably why they had decided to open the castle to the public. Maybe they had fallen on hard times, but if they had, surely the logical thing to do would have been to sell what was without doubt a very valuable piece of real estate, or at least some of the surrounding land.

She was standing there, wondering where the main entrance was, when the sound of a voice attracted her attention.

'This is private property. You're not meant to be in here.'

The owner of the voice was a diminutive but feisty-looking, white-haired old lady, and she was peering

23

suspiciously out of a first-floor window. Alice gave her a little wave.

'Good afternoon, I have an appointment with Simonetta Varaldo. My name's Alice Sterling and I've come from England.'

A less confrontational expression appeared on the elderly lady's face, but she gave no reply, stepping back and closing the window, leaving Alice standing in the courtyard wondering what would happen next.

Less than a minute later a door in the wall, about twenty paces from where she was standing, opened with a creak and a young woman appeared. She gave Alice a friendly wave and beckoned to her.

'Signora Sterling? I'm Simonetta. Do come in.'

As Alice walked across to the doorway, she checked the woman out. From the look of her, they were probably roughly the same age. Simonetta Varaldo had an attractive face and an enviable mass of glossy black hair that hung down past her shoulders. She was wearing jeans and a chunky grey V-neck pullover. Alice also checked out the doorway itself. Set in a sculpted stone archway, the tall double doors were clearly very old and had been carved with a most intricate design of what looked like a wildcat entwined with a snake. The doors were badly in need of a coat of varnish or some wax, but even in their current state this was a spectacular piece of artistry and Alice nodded to herself. If the rest of the castle was as ornate as this, it promised to be popular with visitors.

'Hello, I'm Alice. It's very kind of you to see me at such short notice.'

'Thank you for coming so quickly. That's very good of you.' They shook hands and Simonetta led her into the castle.

Alice found herself in a huge, vaulted entrance hall with massive flagstones covering the floor. It was quite dark in here as the only light came in through narrow windows, one on either side of the doors and four others cut into the opposite wall, each barely wide enough for an archer to fire through. It was also icy cold after the pleasant early spring sunshine outside, and Alice could see why the other woman was wearing a thick pullover. She pulled her jumper tighter around her body and hoped the temperature would be higher on the upper floors.

Corridors led off to the left and right, and ahead of them was a stone staircase, several metres wide. Simonetta made her way up the stairs, and as they climbed, Alice made a point of trying to keep up with the other woman's pace and was delighted to manage it without too much discomfort. The light grew stronger and stronger, so that by the time they reached the first floor, larger windows allowed welcome sunshine to illuminate and warm their surroundings. It still wasn't hot up here by a long way, but it was a much more welcome temperature, particularly after months spent in the draughty corridors of the manor back in England.

Alice took a good look around. While the ground floor had been workmanlike and clearly designed to play a major defensive role, up here there was a distinctly different, more comfortable feel to the place. The floor was no longer rough stone, but covered with black and white marble tiles, each of them two or three feet across, giving a giant chessboard appearance to what was quite a large open landing.

The wall directly opposite was filled with family portraits, mostly of serious-looking men with extravagant facial hair. These had been hung two or three deep across the full width of the landing, and the overall impression was not so much of a portrait gallery as of a medieval advertising hoarding. Standing silhouetted against them was a lone figure and as Alice approached, he stepped forward but didn't speak. The forbidding expression and the bushy white beard could have come from any of the portraits behind him.

Alice walked across to shake hands with him, feeling unusually apprehensive. She introduced herself and braced herself for a crushing handshake, but he was remarkably gentle. He was probably in his late sixties or early seventies and, even though his shoulders were now somewhat hunched forward, he was a tall man exuding a commanding presence. He still didn't say a word, and then a few seconds of awkward silence followed before Simonetta reacted and introduced him.

'This is my father, Barone Lodovico di Varaldo.'

'I'm very pleased to meet you, sir.' Alice wasn't very sure how she should address a member of the Italian nobility, but it didn't seem to matter to him. The baron was no longer looking at her, his eyes now staring out through the leaded glass into the valley below.

'Our family has lived here for five centuries.'

His tone was full of gravitas, but as a conversation starter it didn't immediately prompt a response. Luckily his daughter stepped in. Alice had a feeling that this was probably something Simonetta had to do on a regular basis for her father who looked as if he was, if not on another planet, at least in a different century.

'History and tradition are very important to *Papà*. His whole life is the castle, the family, and the history of the family.'

Alice took her cue. 'Family history is very important to me as well. Our family has lived and worked the same farm for six generations.' The fact that the Sterling family had never owned the farm, but had always been tenant farmers, was something she decided to reveal at a later date. This answer appeared to do the trick, as the baron returned his eyes from the middle distance and surveyed Alice more closely.

'Romano told me you came from good farming stock.' This came as a surprise to Alice. Clearly, Lord Fitzgerald-Chagleigh had spoken about her at length to his friend in London who had then relayed the information to Count Romano, whoever he was. Alice made a mental note to make sure she bought something nice at the duty-free shop on the way back to say thank you to Ronald and Fenella. The baron nodded a few times to give weight to his words. 'Without farmers, where would we be? The salt of the earth.'

'Indeed.'

Alice wondered whether the Varaldo family cultivated any of the land around here or if they kept livestock. It would be interesting to see how large the estate was and how productive it was. She hadn't seen any vineyards or olive groves up here in the hills, nor had she passed many sheep and cattle grazing in the fields. Considering she was now in the Parma ham production area it had come as a surprise to find that she hadn't passed any pig farms either. Cows were essential for parmesan cheese, and pigs of course were the necessary raw material for the world-famous ham, so where were they hiding?

'Shall we all go and sit down? Come on, *Papà*.'

Count Lodovico showed no sign of wanting to follow his daughter and when she actually went over to him and gave his arm a tug, he pulled away irritably and turned his back on both of them. Assuming that he knew why Alice was here, this wasn't a positive sign by any means. Maybe he didn't feel so convinced about the idea of opening the castle to the public as Simonetta. Presumably he was the owner and ultimate arbiter of what happened here at the castle, so if he wasn't interested, this didn't look good at all. Alice found herself wondering if this whole trip had maybe been a waste of time before it had even started.

Leaving him standing there among the pictures of his ancestors, Alice followed Simonetta down a long corridor lined with suits of armour and vicious-looking medieval weapons with a sinking feeling in the pit of her stomach.

Chapter 4

At the end of the corridor was another beautifully carved door and beyond it a huge high-ceilinged living room with windows looking out over the roofs of the town further down the hillside. Alice could see a couple of people walking across the piazza, while a blue and white bus slowly made its way through the narrow streets. She didn't envy the bus driver. It had been tricky enough manoeuvring her little Fiat through the tortuous streets of the town centre, let alone a monster like that, but it did show that tourist coaches should be able to get up to the castle, and that would be a bonus – if the baron agreed to the project, and that looked as if it was by no means certain.

It was noticeably warmer in this room, no doubt due to the roaring log fire in the huge stone fireplace at the far end. It wouldn't be long now until the end of April, and presumably fires would gradually cease to be necessary. She spared a thought for how cold it was likely to be here in the depths of winter. A quick glance around the room revealed no sign of radiators, and she suppressed a little shiver of apprehension. Simonetta led the way across to the fire and they sat down opposite each other. As they did so, a large grey cat which had been relaxing on a rug in front of the fire reluctantly rose to its feet and shot them a disdainful glance before stalking off and disappearing behind one of the aged leather sofas.

Another figure appeared from a smaller door at the far end of the room. She was probably in her sixties and she was dressed from head to foot in black. Simonetta spotted her and glanced across at Alice.

'Have you eaten? Can we offer you something? At least a coffee, or maybe a cup of tea, if you prefer?'

Alice had only had a cup of tea and some biscuits on the flight, but she wasn't really hungry, so she gave Simonetta a grateful smile. 'A cup of real Italian coffee would be wonderful, thank you. That's something I haven't had for ages.'

'I'll have the same, thank you, Ines.'

The lady in black gave a nod and a little smile before turning and disappearing from the room again. As she did so, Simonetta picked up on what Alice had just said. 'You used to live in Italy, didn't you? Your Italian's very fluent, even though I believe you've been back in England for some years now. Is that right?'

Alice nodded and took a deep breath. It was time to tell her tale. Briefly she told Simonetta about the five years she had spent in the Dolomites, and described the sort of work she used to do at the old monastery. Simonetta looked interested as Alice told her about the administrative duties she had had and she nodded in sympathy when Alice told her the reason why she had left.

'I was with a group of friends in the high mountains and we were caught up in an avalanche. My left leg was badly crushed and they had to amputate it below the knee.' She took a deep breath as the memory of that terrible time washed over her yet again, but she did her best to sound confident as she continued. 'It could have been a whole lot worse but I had to give up the job and come home for quite a long period of convalescence.'

'If I hadn't been told that you had a problem with your leg, I wouldn't have noticed. I had no idea it was so serious, but you seem to get around very well.'

Alice felt a little surge of triumph. 'It's okay, thanks. It's taken me a while to get used to the prosthetic, but I manage quite well, although my knee has to do all the work and it aches a bit every now and then. About the only practical problem I have is that I need an automatic car as it was my left leg that was crushed. Otherwise, as long as I don't have to run any marathons, I get by.'

The coffee appeared at that moment, and Alice was able to take a break, greatly heartened by Simonetta's reaction to the disclosure of her disability – very different from that of her former boyfriend. The coffee was brought in by a good-looking young woman probably around the same age as they were, late twenties or early thirties. She was carrying a silver tray and on it were two exquisite little porcelain espresso cups, a very ornate silver coffee pot and a matching plate piled high with what looked like home-made biscuits. Alice murmured her thanks, which were echoed by Simonetta.

'Thank you, Silvia.' The maid nodded and turned away without a word, shooting Alice a curious glance as she did so. Alice caught her eye and gave her a smile and the woman produced a nervous smile in return. Simonetta pointed towards the biscuits. 'Silvia's mother, Ines, makes the best biscuits in the world. These are a local speciality. She's been making them for me since I was a baby. Do try one.'

Alice picked one up and nibbled it, tasting marzipan, honey and hazelnuts. Simonetta was right, it was delightful, and the thought immediately occurred to Alice that a regular supply of home-made biscuits in a café up here in the castle would no doubt be very popular with visitors. She made appreciative noises and was soon on her second biscuit as the interview proceeded. She went into considerable detail about the work she had been doing at the manor back in Devon. She had already decided to tell the truth about her promotion to assistant manager, only for government funding cuts to be about to see her demoted again. Just as with the revelation about her leg, she knew it was important to be honest from the start. In return, Simonetta started to tell Alice more about the castle itself, but a voice from behind interrupted her. Alice turned and saw the baron standing at the door. She hadn't heard him arrive and she wondered how long he'd been standing there.

He launched into a rambling history of the family, but his daughter expertly managed to steer the conversation back to the twenty-first century and asked Alice what she thought of the castle.

'It's a stunning and unique historic building in a fabulous location, and I feel sure if it's done right, it'll prove to be a great success with Italians as well as with foreign tourists.'

She saw Simonetta shoot what looked like a triumphant glance across at the baron but there was nothing in return. Alice found herself wondering if he had even been listening. Undeterred, Simonetta then asked a big question. 'How much do you think it's likely to cost to carry out all the work that'll be necessary?'

Alice shrugged. 'I honestly can't say at this point, but if I can have a look around, I'll have a better idea.'

Simonetta jumped to her feet. 'Absolutely, if you'd like to come with me, I'll give you the tour.' Leaving the baron standing on his own, she led Alice back into the corridor again.

The tour lasted well over half an hour, and by the end of it, Alice was feeling quite overawed. The place was enormous.

When they finally returned to the lounge, Alice was delighted that she had managed to do the whole tour without too much discomfort but it was a relief to have a chance to sit down. The baron was still standing in exactly the same position, but he had turned towards the fire that had died down considerably. He gave no sign of registering their return, his eyes staring deep into the glowing embers. Simonetta knelt down between him and the grey cat, who had emerged from his hiding place, and added a couple of big logs and a handful of kindling. Once the flames had begun to lick up the sides of the fresh logs, she returned to her seat and shot Alice an enquiring glance.

'Well, what do you think now you've had a look around?'

Alice gave her a beaming smile. 'Amazing! Thank you for the tour. It has confirmed my initial impression that this is a very special place indeed.' Out of the corner of her eye she saw the baron turn towards her and felt him scrutinising her as she continued. 'The good news is that to my untrained eye – I did a certain amount of building surveying at university, but I'm not an architect – it looks as though it's all structurally pretty sound, and I couldn't see any significant subsidence or worse. Yes, there's a lot that'll need doing, particularly on general modernising and on the health and safety side, but I didn't see anything that could prove to be disastrous.'

'And the bad news?'

'The cost of it all. Like I say, I'm not an architect, but even hoping that any structural repairs aren't too serious, all the surveys and bureaucratic hoops you'll have to go through in order to get permission to open to the public aren't going to be cheap. For a start, a historic property like this will no doubt come under the remit of the *Belle Arti*.' She heard an exasperated snort from the baron. 'I'm sure you know how difficult they can be.' She had already crossed swords with the Italian state heritage authority when she had been working up in the Dolomites, and she knew they could be pernickety in the extreme, just like their British counterparts. 'I imagine they'll expect you to replace oak with oak, stone with stone and so on, which could cost an awful lot.'

'Can you put a figure on it?' Alice could tell that Simonetta was on edge.

'I can only guess. Until you get a full survey done, it's hard to know. You'll need to employ new staff – not just somebody like me to run things – so you probably need to reckon quite a few hundred thousand euros, maybe a million or more if there's a lot to be done.'

Alice saw Simonetta cast another glance across at her father and this time there appeared to be a pleading look on her face, but the response was the same as before: a blank wall. Was it the expense of the conversion? This would confirm Alice's speculation that the family might be running short of money. She had seen no sign of any great expenditure since her arrival and it was clear the whole place needed serious modernisation. Of course, she told herself, that had to be it: the Varaldo family were broke, or close to it. After all, why throw their home open to the public and risk losing so much of their privacy unless they were being forced into it? And if this was the case, maybe they weren't going to be in a position to fund all the expense. The other thing that was emerging ever more clearly was that while Simonetta looked and sounded enthusiastic at the project, her father appeared to have little or no interest in it. Simonetta finally stood up and glanced at her watch.

'It's almost half past five. I'm afraid I have to go out at six, otherwise we would have invited you to stay for dinner.'

It was looking more and more as though her trip to Italy had been an expensive waste of time. Well, not really a waste of time, she corrected herself; it had been refreshing to come back to Italy after so long. She stood up and addressed both of them.

'That's very kind of you, but I need to get off. I'm flying home again tomorrow and I've booked into a hotel in Parma tonight. I've never been to Parma before, but I saw that it was voted Italy's City of Culture a couple of years ago and I promised myself I'd try to spend a couple of hours looking around the place before going to bed.'

'I'm sure you'll find it a charming city. Don't forget to take a look at the Teatro Regio while you're there. It's one of the most famous opera houses in Italy. You maybe know that Giuseppe Verdi was born not far from here.'

Alice nodded. 'I'm looking forward to seeing it. Thank you both very much for taking the time to see me. It's been fascinating, and I feel sure your home can be turned into a spectacular tourist attraction. Could I just ask when you think you might be able to let me know one way or the other about the position? It's just that I'm applying for other jobs back in the UK, though none of them are anything like as appealing as this one could be.'

'Very soon indeed,' Simonetta cast another despairing glace across at her father, '*Papà*, Alice is going now.'

As if waking from a dream, the baron roused himself and offered Alice his hand. 'Good to meet you… Salt of the earth.' Alice suppressed a smile. It appeared that the baron was not a man of many words.

Simonetta accompanied Alice down the stairs, out through the gatehouse, and across the drawbridge to the car. When they got there, Alice held out her hand, but Simonetta clearly had something to say first.

'I promise I'll be in touch early next week. There's something you need to know about my father. He's not himself these days, I'm afraid. My mother died two years ago, but he still hasn't come to terms with it. Memories of her and the history of the family seem to be his only interests nowadays. He's always been very conscious of the family and its traditions, and it's been an uphill struggle to get him to even start talking about opening the castle to the public.'

'Do you think he'll go along with your plan? Was it your idea?'

'Yes, it was my idea. I don't see that we have any alternative.' Simonetta gave a helpless shrug. 'I really hope he'll agree. My brother's been away but he's coming back tomorrow, so hopefully between the two of us we'll be able to convince Papà… and then of course there's Nonna.

'Your grandmother's the elderly lady I saw when I arrived?'

Simonetta nodded. 'Nonna turned ninety earlier in the year, but she still thinks she rules the roost – and she's probably right. If I can convince her that it's a good idea, I know she'll be able to convince Papà. He always listens to her.'

'And as far as the project's concerned, do you think your brother will agree?'

'I know how to handle Achille. He'll be okay.'

'Is he your little brother?'

'No, he's thirty-five, five years older than me.'

'That makes you and me about the same age. I'm thirty-one. Well, I hope they all like the idea. I'm sure it's the right thing to do. The place has a terrific amount of potential.'

'As you can imagine, it's an enormous undertaking for us, and it'll mean borrowing money, which is always a risk. I know Papà's terrified of losing the castle after the family have been here for so many generations, but if we don't do something soon, we're going to be in severe financial trouble.' She caught hold of Alice's arm. 'I'm sorry, I shouldn't have told you that. Please keep that to yourself.'

'Of course. To be honest, I thought that might be the case. It's all too common with old properties of this size. Just the upkeep from year to year can be financially crippling.'

'Thank you, Alice. I'm very keen to go ahead and I promise I'll press Papà to make a decision.' She transferred her grip to Alice's hand and shook it warmly clasped in both of hers. 'What I can tell you is that we've seen six other potential candidates for the position and, to my mind, you're by far the strongest. If we do decide to go ahead, I would very much like it to be with you.'

Alice drove down the hill with conflicted emotions. She had been delighted to hear Simonetta's parting words but she was still dubious as to whether the baron would go along with the plan. His expression throughout had been far from supportive and she had a horrible feeling that even though Simonetta was clearly keen to go ahead, there was a very real possibility that he might veto it. This at least made Alice realise one thing: if the family did decide to embark on the project of opening the castle to the public, she knew she would very much like to be part of it. The castle was a stunning piece of architecture and she knew that she would relish the challenge of opening it to the twenty-first century.

When she got down to the piazza she parked outside the hotel and sat down at one of the tables outside and stretched her legs. She knew what she needed: a nice cup of tea.

A waitress came out a minute later and Alice asked for a cup of tea with a drop of cold milk. She knew from experience that here in Italy if she didn't specify the milk, the tea would probably arrive with a slice of lemon. As she sat and waited, enjoying the remaining warmth of the late afternoon sunshine, she looked around. The piazza itself was deserted apart from a couple of kids doing their best to use their skateboards on the uneven surface of the square. Alongside her, only two of the other tables were occupied; one by two elderly ladies and the other by a young couple. The atmosphere was calm and not dissimilar in many ways to rural Devonshire. She felt remarkably at home and had a good feeling about this place.

There was a momentary hiccup when the waitress brought the tea and Alice spotted that the tea bag in its little packet on the saucer alongside the cup of hot water was some kind of herbal tea. Luckily Alice had come prepared and dug into her handbag for the proper English teabags she had had the foresight to bring with her. She was sitting there drinking her tea and thinking about all the work that would need to be done to the castle when two men emerged through the door of the bar. One was wearing a white chef's uniform and the two had obviously been talking. They shook hands warmly before the other man turned away. As he did so his eyes briefly met hers and he gave her a hint of a smile. He then walked across to the other side of the road, climbed into a silver sports car and drove off.

Alice watched the car disappear around the corner, all thought of the castle suddenly banished from her mind, now replaced by bewilderment and something more. She was bewildered because she couldn't deny that she had felt a little thrill of attraction as his eyes had met hers. This was bewildering and unexpected because men hadn't been on her radar since the accident four years earlier. She had kept telling herself that this was because down in the wilds of rural Devon the choice of eligible bachelors was severely restricted, but deep down she knew it was because of the accident and what had happened with Maurizio. She was all too conscious of her prosthetic limb, her limp, and the way her self-confidence as far as men were concerned had all but disappeared. Now here she was, only just arrived in the little town, and some random man had already attracted her attention.

Was this a good thing or bad?

Chapter 5

Alice enjoyed her brief stay in Parma – although she got well and truly lost trying to drive into the city centre. Her flight back was uneventful, and she arrived home on Sunday afternoon. After dropping her things at the cottage, she headed to the Dower House with a goodie bag of parmesan cheese, Parma ham, and a bottle of the good, dry Lambrusco for Ronald and Fenella. As she drove through the Devon lanes, she reflected on how different life might be for her if she were to return to Italy. The few hours she had been able to spend looking around Parma had been fascinating. It was a vibrant city with a large population of university students and there was obviously a lot of historical, artistic and architectural interest in the city and in the surrounding area, as well as a wealth of industry. It would certainly make a change from rural Devonshire – although on a pleasant spring evening like this, Devon definitely had its own charm.

As for Varaldo itself, the countryside around the castle had looked delightful, and Simonetta had told her that the estate extended to over a thousand hectares, so there would be ample opportunity maybe even for horse rides if there was a riding stable nearby. However, there still remained a big question mark over whether or not the family would choose to go ahead with the project. The other thing that had been going through her mind for the last twenty-four hours was her unexpected reaction to seeing the fair-haired man. She was still trying to work out what this might mean to her. The odds were that she would never see that man again but she drew considerable consolation from the fact that she had felt that spark of attraction. Maybe the shadow of her accident and the equally grim shadow of Maurizio were finally beginning to melt away. She certainly hoped so.

Doing her best to relegate this fleeting encounter to the back burner, she found herself hoping that the baron and the rest of his family would decide to go ahead with the project. In so many ways it sounded like the perfect job for her.

This was just about the first question Fenella asked her. 'Well, did they offer you the job, and did you say yes?'

'No, they're still making up their minds, but they promised to let me know very soon.'

'And if they do offer you the job, what's your answer going to be?'

Alice had had time to debate this by now and, in spite of her fears, she had reached a decision. 'I would say yes like a shot. I was only in Italy for twenty-four hours, but I had time to wander around Parma on my own and I enjoyed myself, apart from getting lost a few times. Later on, I went to a restaurant where I had a wonderful meal, and it all felt familiar and comfortable.' She looked across at the two of them and shrugged. 'If they do offer it to me, I just hope I'll be up to the task. It certainly isn't going to be easy. Apart from everything that'll need to be done and all the bureaucratic complications that I'm sure will come up, there's a serious question mark over whether the baron's heart is in it.'

She went on to tell them all about the area, the little town and the castle itself. She was still in full flow, describing the building in minute detail and showing them the photos she had taken, when her phone bleeped to tell her she had a message.

> Dear Alice. My father and brother have agreed. We're going to go ahead with the project, and we would like you to be our new Castle Manager. We do hope you'll say yes. I'll send you an e-mail with a detailed offer. Simonetta Varaldo

Alice rattled off a quick translation for Ronald and Fenella and then looked up from the screen, beaming at them. She could feel a wave of excitement rising up inside her and she had to suppress a little yelp of delight. Simonetta had managed to talk her father around and she felt herself grinning like an idiot.

'That's it. They've offered me the job, and unless there's something significantly different in the offer when I get it, I'm going to say yes.'

Fenella turned to her husband who was standing by the sherry bottle. 'I think this calls for champagne, Ronald, don't you?'

'I certainly do.'

He headed for the kitchen to get a bottle from the fridge and, while he was away, his wife reached across and caught hold of Alice's hand. 'I know you're doing the right thing, Alice. Just you wait and see. It's a whole new life opening up for you. I envy you, I really do.'

Alice gave her a smile and waved her hand at her surroundings. 'You wouldn't ever want to leave all this, would you?'

'I love this house, and I love this part of Devon, but the idea of being able to get my teeth into a new project would be very appealing. I tell you this: when Varaldo castle opens to the public, I promise we'll be among the very first visitors. You're going to have a lot of fun, I just know it.'

Over glasses of champagne they chatted about Italy, Parma, and how Alice's life was going to change as a result of this new job. Alice invited them to come and visit her once she had got herself settled. She knew she would miss these lovely friendly people but, hopefully, she would stay in touch with them as well as making new friends in Italy.

As it started to grow dark she went back home and just as she got there she received the promised e-mail from Simonetta. Before clicking on it, she realised that she was feeling apprehensive; she knew that this wasn't fear of taking the job, but fear that something in the e-mail might result in her *not* taking the job. If she had needed any proof that this was something she really wanted to do, her nervousness provided it.

She took a deep breath and opened the e-mail. Scanning through it, she was pleased to see that it looked as though they were offering her a lot of freedom to do what she felt she needed to do, rather than being too prescriptive. Yes, big decisions about expenditure would have to be approved by the 'whole' family which sounded a bit ominous, but for the day-to-day, they were giving her a refreshingly free rein. It came as no surprise to see that they hoped she would be able to get things moving quickly, so that they could open the castle to the public as soon as possible, but she was relieved to read that they acknowledged that this would depend on a number of factors, many of them out of Alice's hands. The experience Alice had already gained of Italian bureaucracy made her fear that delays were going to be inevitable, but she felt sure the family would already be aware of this.

To her delight, she saw that the starting salary they were offering was bang in the middle of the range they had previously mentioned and so would represent a considerable increase compared to what she had been getting as assistant manager here at the manor. Even better, they would provide a car for her. Simonetta kindly indicated that this would be an automatic and Alice was touched that she had remembered. They stated that they would like her to start as soon as possible and stressed that this job wasn't just about organising the conversion of the castle into a tourist attraction but was a long term offer of employment. They hoped that Alice would settle down and put down roots back in Italy again. The last paragraph was very welcome and resolved one of the things which had been worrying Alice.

> As far as accommodation is concerned, a lady in the town has a small, furnished, ground-floor apartment that she would be happy to rent to you at a reasonable rate. You may have other plans but if you would like me to get more details about this, please let me know, and I'll get this back to you as soon as possible.

Alice slumped onto a chair and breathed deeply. The gloom she had been feeling ever since that meeting with Helen from HR disappeared without trace and she felt a smile forming on her face. The job was hers if she wanted it.

And she did. Yes, it was going to be a real challenge and she hoped she would be able to justify Simonetta's confidence in her, but she knew it was something she wanted to do; for them and, above all, for herself.

First thing on Monday morning, Alice gave in her notice to Marjorie who told her she would be sorely missed and then came up with an excellent suggestion. A friend of hers had been looking for a little cottage to rent in the area but without success. Alice worked out that if she rented her house to this lady when she left the country, the regular monthly income would allow her to keep up the mortgage payments. She had no idea at this stage whether her new life in Italy might be going to last weeks, months or years, so it seemed prudent to hang on to a toehold on the UK property ladder, in case she came hurrying back with her tail between her legs.

She then spent hours on the phone sorting out all sorts of practical matters ranging from cancelling utility contracts to arranging for her mail to be forwarded to her mum and dad at the farm. She went to see her parents at the end of the week and told them all about it. They were both very supportive and her mum asked all sorts of questions, principal among which was this one: 'It sounds like an exciting job, are they nice people?'

'Very nice, particularly the daughter.'

'Who else is there in the family? Did you say the mother died some time ago?'

'Yes, two years ago, I believe. There's Simonetta, the daughter, who's probably about my age, the father who's a bit vague – not doolally, but definitely a bit woolly and from what Simonetta told me, a stickler for tradition – and there's a brother as well, but I haven't met him yet. Oh yes, and there's also the ninety-year-old grandmother, a housekeeper and a maid. Even assuming there are a few more living or working there as well, it's still not that many people to be rattling around in a huge property even bigger than Fitzgerald-Chagleigh Manor.'

'How much land have they got, and do they farm it?' It came as no surprise to Alice to find that her dad was more interested in that side of things.

'On the information sheet they sent me, it says the total area of the estate is twelve hundred hectares. I make that about three thousand acres, right?'

Her father's eyes opened wide. 'That's a lot of land.' He produced a wry smile. 'You could get this farm and half a dozen others like it into that area. What stock do they keep or are they arable?'

'A lot of the land is forest and it's very hilly, but I really don't know if they do much farming at all. I didn't see any sheep or cattle close by. In fact, I didn't see much in the way of livestock anywhere around there. That's one of the first things I want to look at. If they're short of cash, it would make sense to start working the land. Don't be surprised if I'm on the phone to you asking for help, Dad. By the way, how are the ostriches working out?'

Her father had always been keen to try out new methods, crops and livestock. Ostrich farming in one of the fields was his latest venture, but Alice knew from her mum that this hadn't been without its problems. She saw him grimace.

'Have you seen the size of the things? Even the dogs are afraid to go in the field with them. I think it's unlikely I'll be expanding the flock any time soon.' He shot her a grin. 'That's a thought: you should be able to keep all sorts of exotic animals over there in Italy where it's warmer. You could always open your own safari park.'

'Firstly, the castle's in the foothills of the Apennines and I imagine it gets very cold there in winter so I'm not sure how lions and giraffes would get on but, more than that, can you imagine the bureaucratic and practical headaches involved in opening a safari park? It's going to be tough enough just making sure visitors to the castle don't trip and fall over, let alone preventing them from being eaten by wild animals. No, Dad, thanks for the thought, but I think I'll keep the safari park idea in reserve for now.'

Chapter 6

At the end of May, Alice drove over to Italy in the little Mini she had bought four years earlier. It had already been pretty old when she had bought it, and she was relieved that it managed the journey without mishap. The trip itself took two full days and cost a lot more than her air ticket to Bologna the previous month had done, but because she had to bring clothes and all the other bits and pieces she would need for a prolonged stay, she had no choice in the matter. As they had told her she would have a car provided, she wasn't quite sure what to do with this one, but she would cross that bridge when she came to it – as long as it got her there. When she finally turned onto the narrow road up the valley towards the castle and got her first sight of it on the hillside ahead she was filled with mixed emotions: relief at having got here intact, coupled with considerable apprehension for what now awaited her.

Simonetta had sent over the details of the apartment to rent in Varaldo, so Alice drove straight there. She hadn't been sure what to expect and it came as a welcome relief to find that this was in a pleasant, if bland, small nineteen-seventies block of four apartments just on the edge of the small town. She drew up outside, climbed out of the car and stretched. Her leg was feeling a bit stiff but after two days of driving that was to be expected. She went up to the front door and saw that set into the wall alongside the door was a panel with four bell pushes. Beside each was a name and it was immediately clear that the four flats all belonged to the same family. The names were: Rossi Francesco, Rossi Antonio, Rossi Guido and Rossi Emilio. Simonetta had given Alice the name Luisella Rossi, so she was momentarily puzzled. While she was still standing there, debating which bell to ring, she heard a car pull up behind her. The door slammed and she heard a voice.

'Signora Sterling?'

Alice turned to see a friendly looking lady carrying a big bag of groceries in each hand.

'Good afternoon. Are you Signora Luisella Rossi?'

The lady came up to the door and set her bags down at her feet before holding out her hand towards Alice. 'That's me. Did you have a good journey? It's a terribly long way from England, isn't it?'

'It was a long drive, but I've seen some beautiful scenery and the trip wasn't too tiring. I've just been trying to work out which of the doorbells belongs to you.'

'My husband and I live on the top floor. He's Francesco and I'm Luisella. My brother-in-law and his wife have the other top floor flat and his son Guido and his wife live on the ground floor. Your apartment's opposite theirs. It used to belong to my father-in-law, Emilio. He passed away two months ago and we haven't changed the name on the bell yet. Do come inside and I'll show you where everything is. Just let me take these groceries upstairs first.'

Alice insisted on helping Luisella carry her bags up the stairs to the first floor and they were greeted at the door of the apartment by an elderly terrier who eyed

Alice suspiciously before waddling over to sniff her hand. Reassured that she didn't smell too bad, the dog began to wag its tail and Luisella nodded approvingly.

'Geronimo likes you. That's good. He's a good judge of character. Come in and let me make you a cup of coffee, or would you like something cold?'

'A coffee would be wonderful, thanks.' Alice sat down at the kitchen table and the little dog came and joined her. She scratched his ears as Luisella filled a much-used moka coffee pot and set it on the stove. As Luisella started putting away the groceries, they chatted and Alice asked about shops and shopping in the area. Luisella was a mine of information.

'Tonino in the minimarket in the piazza stocks a bit of everything, and the baker makes wonderful cakes as well as bread, and if Vincenzo in the hardware shop doesn't have it, you don't need it. It's like a labyrinth in there. I tend to do a big shop once a week at the supermarket down in the main valley. You can't miss it. Anyway, knowing you were coming, I've bought you some basics to get you started. Here...' She placed one of the bags on the floor alongside Alice who was quick to thank her and offer to pay, but Luisella waved away her money and her thanks.

'You're very welcome. Call it a housewarming present.' The coffee pot started bubbling on the stove and Luisella brought it over to the table and filled two little cups with steaming hot black coffee. Along with it she produced a tin of biscuits that looked very similar to those made by Ines up at the castle. Clearly this was the traditional local variety that appealed to people here in the valley. Luisella took a seat opposite Alice and offered her a biscuit. 'I understand from Simonetta that you're going to be working up at the castle. She told me they're hoping to open it to the public. How exciting.' She lowered her voice and looked around almost furtively. 'Of course, not everybody's happy at the idea.'

Alice's ears pricked up. 'Is that so? I would have thought people would welcome the prospect of new job opportunities, and maybe being able to make some extra money from tourists.'

'Some people are never happy, always complaining about something. They're saying this'll bring in more cars and maybe coaches as well, and cause chaos on the roads.'

'Would you say that's the opinion of the majority of the people around here or just a few?' Alice remembered how important the local mayor could be in small communities like this. 'What about the town authorities? What does the mayor think?'

Luisella shook her head. 'I'm afraid he's the ringleader and it's nothing to do with traffic or anything like that. The fact is that Cesare, the mayor, is a Montorso, and they've been fighting the Varaldo family for centuries. Even if Baron Lodovico was offering to build a new hospital or donate a million euros to the town, I'm sure Cesare would be against it just on principle. You know how it is: these feuds go way back, and after so long people probably can't even remember why they're fighting, but they still do.'

'So the Montorso family and the Varaldo family are at daggers drawn...' Alice shook her head slowly as she digested this news. This could be awkward. 'Where does the mayor live? Is there another castle around here some-where? I haven't seen one.'

'There used to be one centuries ago, but there's nothing left now except a pile of rubble. The Montorso family still have a farm and a lot of land, but no castle. Cesare Montorso farms over on the other side of the valley. You'll be able to see the farmhouse from the castle. It's a long red brick building surrounded by fields.'

Alice weighed up what she had just heard. In order to get all the permits the castle would need, she felt sure not having the support of the local mayor could prove to be a major impediment. Maybe she could play the part of neutral peacemaker but, if the two families had been fighting for centuries, it was going to be an uphill struggle to bring such a long-standing feud to an end. She suppressed a sigh. She hadn't even started work yet and she had already encountered what might prove to be an insurmountable obstacle.

Once they had finished their coffees, Luisella led Alice downstairs and showed her the flat where she would be spending the next few months. To Alice's relief, it was clean and comfortable and the furniture was functional and more than sufficient for her needs. She even had her own little piece of lawned garden at the rear of the property and from there she could look directly up and see the tops of the towers of the castle on the hillside above. She reckoned she should easily be able to walk up there in ten or fifteen minutes, so she wouldn't need to use a car every day and it would be valuable exercise, just like the physio kept telling her. Before Luisella left, Alice asked her about the restaurant she had spotted in the piazza and received a positive review.

'The Casa Rosa's very good. Giorgio who owns it used to work in one of the really posh restaurants in Venice and now his son is taking over in the kitchen, but Giorgio still keeps an eye on things. Why don't you go there this evening and see what it's like, or maybe you prefer to have an early night after your long drive? I've bought ham and cheese and salad for you and there's fresh bread.' She opened a cupboard door revealing two huge two-litre bottles of red wine without labels. 'That's good. Francesco said he'd put some wine in for you. He gets it from a man in the Veneto region and it's very good. The water here's perfectly pure so you can drink from the tap.'

'That's really kind of you and your husband, thank you so much.' Alice glanced at her watch. It was almost six o'clock. 'I must say though that the idea of a good meal cooked by somebody else and then an early night sounds perfect. What time do you think the restaurant opens?'

'Well, the bar's open all day, but the restaurant starts serving at seven, so if you go in then you should be able to have a meal and still get your early night.'

By the time Alice had finished unloading the car and unpacking her things it was almost seven and she headed off on foot to the Casa Rosa. Although she had left cool, damp weather in England, here in Varaldo it was a pleasantly warm, late May day. She took off her jumper and slung it over her shoulders as she walked. It took barely ten minutes to get into the centre of the little town and she enjoyed checking out the various houses as she went along. The closer to the centre she got, the older the buildings became, and she saw that many of them had probably started life as smallholdings and still had an agricultural connection. Almost all of them had a courtyard, many had a noisy barking dog, and she counted at least half a dozen tractors. Farming was clearly still an important part of local life.

Just before she reached the main square, she passed a fine old stone building with an Italian flag fluttering from the façade. Above the door was a sign indicating that this was the *Municipio*, the town hall. She had a feeling she might end up spending quite a lot of time inside this building and she hoped the mayor wouldn't cause too many problems for her but, from what Luisella had just said, this seemed like a forlorn hope. She carried on into Piazza San Giovanni and checked her watch. It was just after seven, so she headed straight for the restaurant.

This was a large old building, constructed of sun-bleached red bricks which presumably were the reason why it was called the Pink House. Across the façade, the words Hotel Restaurant had been painted in white and Alice wondered how much business they did up here. Of course, if the valley was still being used by pilgrims on the Pilgrims' Way, then presumably there had to be a certain amount of passing trade – at least in the summer.

Most of the tables outside on the cobbles were occupied and she attracted a number of curious glances from the customers enjoying a Sunday evening drink. She walked into the bar and was greeted by the same friendly looking waitress from before who directed her through a fly curtain into the restaurant. Although it was early, three of the tables were already occupied. A circular table housed a noisy family gathering of seven or eight adults and half a dozen little children; another table was occupied by a couple of pensioners, and a fair-haired man was sitting on his own in the far corner, doing something on a laptop. As her eyes landed on him, she did a double take. She could only see his face side on, but there could be no doubt about it: it was the mystery man she had seen when she was last here. So much for him being a ship passing in the night. It looked as if he might be a regular client here. So what might that mean for her?

A tall waiter led her to a small table in the opposite corner from the fair-haired man. While she waited for the waiter to bring the menu, sight of the man's laptop reminded her that she hadn't asked about Wi-Fi at the apartment. She pulled out her phone and saw that there was good signal here so she sent a short message to her mum to reassure her that she had arrived safe and well. She had just pressed Send when the waiter returned with a jug of water, a basket of bread and a copy of the menu. He asked if he could get her anything else to drink and, considering that all she was going to do was to walk home and go straight to bed at the end of the meal, she asked for a small carafe of local red wine. She told herself she might as well start acclimatising right now.

When the waiter returned to take her order she opted for mixed antipasti followed by home-made *tortelli di erbette alla parmigiana*. He explained that these tiny ravioli-like pasta pockets were filled with local herbs, spinach, ricotta cheese and, of course, parmesan. Alice felt sure she wouldn't need a main course after this and the waiter gave her a little smile.

'If you find you have room for a dessert, the chef makes a wonderful semifreddo with *zabaione* and hazelnuts. See how much appetite you have left after the pasta.'

Alice's taste buds told her that she might well be able to find room for what sounded like a delightful dessert.

She poured herself half a glass of dark red wine and sipped it slowly as she looked around. The noisy children at the round table had suddenly been silenced by the arrival of plates of pasta. The elderly couple on the other table were sitting in complete silence, but it didn't look like uncomfortable silence. As she directed her attention towards the man with the laptop in the far corner he looked up and their eyes met for a moment. There might have been a hint of recognition on his face and he gave her a little smile. She hastily dropped her eyes to her glass, but she couldn't ignore the same spark of attraction that shot through her.

He was wearing a T-shirt and jeans with what looked like big black boots on his feet, but he didn't look as if he was a manual worker. He was very good-looking, but nobody who looked like he did would be interested in her once he knew her secret. That was the hard lesson she had learnt from Maurizio. Years ago, she had found herself not quite fighting the men off, but she had always had male company. Since the accident, everything had changed. She had gradually come to terms with it, but that didn't make it any more palatable.

Several minutes later, when her eyes momentarily flicked across to him again, she realised that the big black boots were in fact a large black dog lying across the man's feet. The man was concentrating on his computer, but this time, as if sensing that it was being watched, the dog raised its head and made eye contact with her, and she smiled at it. She'd always liked dogs – her parents had always kept them on the farm – and she had a soft spot for Labradors in particular. Raising her eyes again, the smile still on her face, she suddenly found that the dog's master was looking straight at her and smiling. Fortunately, at that moment the waiter intervened.

'Your antipasti, signora. *Buon appetito.*'

Alice murmured her thanks and concentrated on the food on her plate – and there was a lot of it. Needless to say, there was hand-carved Parma ham and along with it there were also three or four different types of sliced salami. Around the meat were neat heaps of pickled cauliflower, carrots and red peppers, wild mushrooms in olive oil and sundried tomatoes. Unusual little fried squares of pasta and a bowl of rocket leaves with oil and balsamic vinegar, sprinkled with slivers of parmesan cheese, completed the spread. It all tasted as good as it looked and Alice took her time, savouring the different but complementary tastes. It was delightful.

She deliberately kept her eyes on her food. All the time the thought that stubbornly refused to shift itself from her head was that she felt drawn to this unknown man. Of course, she told herself firmly, surely there was no great difference between appreciating the beauty of a building or a painting and admiring the physical appearance of a man or, indeed, a woman. The fact that she liked the look of this man didn't have to mean anything more than aesthetic appreciation.

Did it?

She kept on eating, eyes locked on her plate, and did her best to think of her first day in her new job that would be starting in little over twelve hours' time. For a moment, the butterflies threatened to return to her stomach, but she did her best to focus on her meal for now. There would be time to worry about work in the morning. Besides, she currently had something else – or some*one* else – on her mind. When she finally summoned the courage to look up from her plate and caught sight of him and his dog again, that same little electric charge ran through her. Before he could look up, she hastily dropped her eyes, reached for her wine glass and drained it in one, almost choking herself in the process. She had been expecting all manner of things to happen here in Italy but not this. She told herself it was probably just the effect of the glass of wine, but her subconscious treated that suggestion with the disdain it merited.

As a displacement activity she pulled out her phone again and checked out the local map, searching for the farm belonging to Cesare Montorso, the mayor of Varaldo and the sworn enemy of the baron and his family. It didn't take long to find and she zoomed in on it. A gravel track led off to the left just as the road from down the valley reached the town, and the farm with its outbuildings lay about two or three hundred metres further along. By going into Street View she saw that this was perched on a hillside, on almost the same level as the castle on the opposite side of the valley. She found herself imagining the warring families surveying each other over the roofs of the town back through the centuries. She wondered what had started the feud, but it must have been something major and significant for the bad feelings to have lasted so long.

Her thoughts were interrupted by the arrival of a huge plate of *tortelli* and she dedicated herself to the pasta for the next ten minutes. By the time she had cleared the plate she knew that she had done the right thing in deciding not to have a main course. She was feeling pleasantly full – but not so full that she was unable to face a portion of the chef's special semifreddo. Once the waiter had removed her empty plate, she picked up her phone and sent a brief text to Simonetta, telling her she had arrived safe and well and asking what time they were expecting her next day. She received an answering call almost immediately.

'Welcome to Varaldo, Alice. How was your journey?'

Alice told her how it had gone and thanked her again for finding her the apartment. She then asked Simonetta something that had been troubling her.

'Please, so I don't make a fool of myself when I meet your grandmother again, can you tell me how I should address her? And your father for that matter. He's a baron and presumably your grandfather was also a baron so should I refer to your grandmother and your father as Your Excellency or something like that?'

'Nonna would chew your head off if you started doing that, although Papà probably wouldn't even notice. No, if you're talking to them just call them Signore and Signora, or if you want to be very polite you can call her Lady Varaldo or even Lady Beatrice. Like I say, Papà wouldn't even notice, but if it's a more formal written communication, then you'd better refer to my father as Barone Lodovico di Varaldo, even though titles mean nothing in Italy anymore.' Alice heard her give a little laugh. 'Unless you're trying to convince a police officer not to give you a speeding ticket.'

'Thanks for clearing that up. And what about your brother? Presumably he'll be the next Baron Varaldo. What should I call him? Come to think of it, are you happy if I call you Simonetta?'

'Of course I am, and Achille's just Achille. Everybody in the town calls us by our first names. We attended the same local elementary school as everybody else.'

Having cleared that up, Alice checked what time she was wanted in the morning and they arranged that she would go in early so as to have the opportunity to talk to Simonetta first, before facing the rest of the family.

The semifreddo was every bit as good as the waiter had said and Alice enjoyed every spoonful. Finally, as she sat back and sipped an espresso, she allowed herself to raise her eyes and shoot a quick glance across the room towards the table with the man and the dog.

But the table was empty.

The man and the Labrador had left and she didn't know whether to feel relief or disappointment. What she was definitely feeling was bewilderment. How strange that just about the first man she had clapped eyes on here in Varaldo had aroused feelings in her of a kind that had been so completely absent from her life for so long.

Chapter 7

After a remarkably good night's sleep, Alice walked up to the castle next morning at eight o'clock on the dot. It was a steep climb but she surprised herself by finding it relatively easy. Yes, her knee ached a bit, but not seriously, and she took this to be a very good sign. Maybe Varaldo would prove to be good for her health, not just for her career.

Nothing much appeared to have changed in the month since she had last been here. The muddy ditch which used to be the moat was still full of junk, the rusty portcullis was still hanging precariously over her head as she walked in through the gatehouse, and the three vehicles were parked in almost exactly the same places at the end of the courtyard. She wondered if one of these would be the car they had promised to her. There was one change, however: a fourth vehicle was now parked alongside the others. Unlike the fairly battered and utilitarian appearance of the Land Rover and the two little Fiats, this was a bright, shiny blue saloon. Alice wondered whether maybe this belonged to Simonetta's brother, Achille. She smiled as she recalled his name and for a moment she wondered if he would appear at the door like the legendary Achilles, carrying a sword and wearing a Grecian helmet. It certainly wasn't a very common man's name in the twenty-first century and she had a suspicion that there was probably some long-standing family history connected with it. Hopefully he wouldn't have an Achilles' heel like the Greek hero that would lead to his ultimate downfall.

She headed for the door in the right-hand wall, but before she got there the same window on the first floor opened, and the same white-haired old lady peered out, only this time she looked less antagonistic.

'Good morning. You're the English girl, aren't you? I remember you.'

Alice gave her a beaming smile as she looked up. 'Good morning, yes, I'm Alice. I'm not too early, am I?'

'Of course not. I've been up for ages. Wait there and I'll come and let you in.'

Alice had to wait almost two minutes before she heard hesitant footsteps on the other side of the door. There was a rattling of a chain and the sound of several locks being turned before the door opened with a creak. Seen close up, Simonetta's grandmother was tiny, her shoulders hunched so much that her head appeared to be permanently facing downwards, but she managed to lift her eyes to Alice's face.

'Good morning, again. Do come in.' She stepped to one side as Alice entered and as she did so, a grey shadow slipped in between their legs. 'And good morning to you, Baffo. Have you caught lots of mice?'

The cat, now that it was safely inside the building, paused and sat down to lick its front paws. It gave Alice a wary look before heading up the stairs, no doubt looking forward to a rest after a night on the tiles. The door closed behind them and Alice turned and held out her hand.

'Thank you for letting me in, Lady Varaldo. I'm very pleased to meet you.'

The baroness transferred her walking stick from her right hand to her left and gave Alice's hand a surprisingly firm shake before indicating the staircase. 'If you'd like to come upstairs, I'll see if Ines can make us some coffee. You go on ahead by all means. I'm afraid I'm not so good at stairs these days.' Her tone wasn't so much apologetic as frustrated. Alice's heart went out to her and she responded with a smile.

'It's a wide staircase. I'd be happy to walk up with you.' She let her smile broaden. 'I'm not sure I'll be much faster than you on the stairs.'

The old lady nodded sagely. 'Of course. Simonetta said your leg was crushed in an avalanche. How awful for you. Well, let's attack the stairs together, shall we?'

Alice felt fingers grip her forearm. No words were exchanged, and they started to make their way slowly up the stairs. They were almost halfway up when the baroness started talking.

'I'm not sure who's up and about yet. I'm afraid my son doesn't surface until mid-morning some days.' She glanced across at Alice who was still working out that the old lady was referring to the baron. 'He's never been an early morning person, and over the past year or two he's been getting worse.' There was more pity than disapproval in her voice and Alice was reminded of what Simonetta had told her about how badly affected her father had been by the death of his wife.

'What about Simonetta's brother? When I was here last time, I didn't meet him. Is he here now?'

This time there was distinctly a disapproving note in Lady Beatrice's voice when she replied. 'Yes, he's here all right. He woke up the whole place in the middle of the night with that blasted car of his. Young people can be so inconsiderate.'

Considering that Alice was thirty-one and Achille four years older than that, 'young' was pushing it a bit, but to somebody of ninety, it probably did seem like they were kids. 'Does he live here full time?' She saw Lady Beatrice nod. 'What does he do?'

'Not very much.' Maybe realising that she might be overstepping the mark in talking about her grandson in derogatory terms to a near stranger who was only an employee, the old lady added some clarification. 'He's in the insurance business, but he doesn't have a fixed work schedule. It'll be interesting to see whether he has to go down to Parma this morning or whether he'll do like his father and have a long lie-in.'

Seeing as the two of them were still alone, Alice took advantage of the moment to ask a question that had been in her head for the last month. 'And Simonetta, does she work?'

'She used to teach Italian literature at the university in Parma but she gave it up two years ago when her mother died, so that she could come and look after her father.'

They turned the corner and as they climbed the last few steps, Simonetta herself appeared at the top and gave them both a smile.

'Good morning, Alice, I see Nonna hasn't wasted any time in putting you to work.'

'Hello, Simonetta. That wasn't work. Your grandmother and I have just been having a nice chat while we climbed the stairs.'

The baroness gave her granddaughter a rueful smile. 'You wait until you're my age, Simonetta. You'll take all the help you can get, I promise you. Which reminds me of something I've been thinking about: when we have tourists coming to visit the castle, we're going to need a lift, maybe two. These days places like this need to be accessible to all.' She glanced across and Alice distinctly saw her wink at her. 'A lift could be very useful, couldn't it?'

Alice grinned at her and nodded. She was impressed. Lady Varaldo's knees might be a bit shaky, but there didn't appear to be anything wrong with her brain. Simonetta clearly felt the same way and she nodded her head enthusiastically. 'Of course, Nonna, that's a very good idea.' She glanced across at Alice. 'We must make sure we include Nonna in our planning meetings. She's full of good ideas.'

Alice nodded in agreement. 'Absolutely. On the subject of planning, I've got all sorts of questions for you all, and I've drawn up a provisional agenda for an initial meeting – unless you already have a list of topics to discuss – hopefully with the whole family if you're all available.'

'I've told my father and my brother that they need to be up early this morning – well, early by their standards – and I wonder if you and I, Alice, could sit down together first and have a general talk before they come along. I've told them the meeting will be at ten o'clock sharp and I've asked Ines to make sure she wakes them and she doesn't let them go back to sleep again. That gives us a couple of hours and, Nonna, you're going to join us, aren't you? There's coffee in the sitting room.'

They walked along the corridor to the sitting room. The early morning sun was streaming in through the windows and the monumental fireplace was empty. It was definitely cooler in here than outside but not nearly as cold as it had been a month before. Still, Alice was glad she had thought to bring a jumper. The baroness shooed the cat off what was presumably both her and the cat's favourite armchair and sat down heavily, resting her stick against the arm. Interestingly, the cat didn't protest. Presumably he, like everybody else in the castle, knew that the baroness was not to be trifled with.

No sooner had they sat down than the door at the far end opened and Silvia, the maid, appeared carrying a tray bearing the same ornate coffee pot as last time and a basket of croissants which smelt wonderful. Today there was another smaller jug alongside these which contained hot milk, and Alice noticed that the cups were larger than the small espresso cups they had used the previous time. Clearly, breakfast demanded the option of milk in coffee. After seeing that they were all served – Alice chose to put milk in her coffee but the baroness just opted for a small black coffee – Simonetta sat back and looked across at Alice.

'Welcome to Varaldo. I'm so glad you were able to accept the job. I'm sure you're the person we need.'

'Well, thank you for offering me the position. It's going to be exciting. Have there been any developments since I was last here? Was it a struggle to get your father and your brother onside?'

'Achille, no. Papà, a bit of a struggle, but with Nonna's help he came around.'

The baroness joined the conversation. 'My son doesn't like change. You have to understand that about him. His father, God bless him, was exactly the same, and that's the main reason we find ourselves having to take such a drastic step now.' She shook her head sadly. 'If my husband had been a bit more commercially minded, things would be a lot different.'

Alice was impressed at how pragmatic the old lady sounded. 'When you say commercially minded, what sort of thing did you have in mind? Opening the castle to the public years ago or something else?'

'I confess that none of us had thought of opening to the public until Simonetta came up with the idea.' She gave her granddaughter another little smile. 'Agriculture is what I've always said we should do, but they've always been against it.'

Simonetta added a bit of explanation. 'As you know, the family's been here for many centuries, and back in medieval and Renaissance times they were the de facto rulers of all this area. People travelling up and down the valley – merchants, pilgrims and others – all had to pay for the right to do so and the family grew rich as a result. Of course that all stopped a long time ago and we've slowly been running out of resources ever since.'

'So why not make money from the land that you own, like your grandmother says? My father makes a decent living out of a farm that's far smaller than what you have here. All right, my dad's farm is almost all workable, productive flat land, and here in the hills it's going to be more difficult, but I can't help noticing that you have many hundreds of hectares of woodland. The price of timber has shot up over the last few years. I'm sure that's something to be looked at.' She saw Simonetta and her grandmother exchange approving looks and pressed on with her ideas. 'Also, so close to Parma, what about milk for parmesan cheese or pigs for ham?'

'All excellent ideas, Alice,' Simonetta replied, a note of regret creeping into her voice. 'But you have to try to understand the mindset of my father and his forebears. Doing something like that would turn us into mere farmers.' She held up her hands in apology. 'No offence to your father, I'm just trying to put you in the picture as far as Varaldo family tradition is concerned. In the eyes of my father and his father before him this would make us no better than the Montorso family.' She caught Alice's eye. 'Have you heard that name before?'

Alice nodded, there was no point pretending. 'Until last night, no, but I was talking to Signora Rossi and she told me some of the story, and how the current mayor is deliberately being obstructive. I must admit to being amazed that a feud that started over half a millennium ago should still continue to this day.'

'I know. It must sound crazy to you. It still sounds crazy to me, and I've lived with it all my life.' Simonetta picked up her cup of coffee and held it out towards Alice in a mock toast. 'Well, here's hoping some fresh blood will be able to knock a bit of sense into them, but don't hold your breath.'

She took a mouthful of coffee and sat back, leaving Alice mulling over what she had just heard. It was beginning to make sense. Ever since being offered the job she had been racking her brains to work out why so much land was not being worked, and now she knew the answer: simple, old-fashioned prejudice, coupled with a misplaced sense of tradition. She felt sure Simonetta was right and that she was going to find herself with an uphill struggle to push change through.

Chapter 8

The three of them chatted for well over an hour and Alice learned more and more about the history of the family, the town and the whole area. Apparently the castle was situated on the Via Francigena, an ancient pilgrimage route that led all the way from Canterbury in England to Rome, and Alice wondered if that might help to get more visitors to the castle when they opened to the public. The subject of the Montorso family was not brought up again, but Alice knew that it would be lurking in the background to everything she did while she was here. They were still talking when the door opened and a tall, dark-haired man walked in. The resemblance to his father quite remarkable and Simonetta hardly needed to make the introductions. .

'Alice, this is my brother, Achille.' She pointed to the clock on the mantlepiece and adopted a hectoring, if affectionate, tone. 'Nine-thirty, this is early for you, Achille. Come and meet our new castle manager, Alice Sterling.'

He walked over to where Alice was sitting and she stood up to shake hands with him. 'I'm very pleased to meet you.' She avoided calling him anything for now and Simonetta must have noticed.

'Alice, do call him by his first name. That's all right with you, isn't it, Achille?'

'Of course, and may I call you Alice?' He was a good-looking man but, interestingly, Alice felt no spark of attraction like the one she had felt for the anonymous man the previous evening. On the one hand it was reassuring to her that she hadn't suddenly developed into a maneater, but it just made what she had felt the previous evening even more inexplicable. Hastily returning her attention to the present, she gave him a smile and a nod. 'Yes, of course, please call me Alice.' She looked across at the baroness. 'And the same applies to you, please, Lady Varaldo.'

A minute later the maid reappeared from the kitchen with more coffee and a pile of her mother's home-made biscuits and Alice was struck yet again by how beautiful she was in a discreet, understated way. As the woman set the tray down on the table, she shot a brief glance across at Achille. Alice was no great expert on human emotions, but she felt sure she had caught affection or more in that brief glance. More interesting still was the fact that an answering expression of tenderness appeared on Achille's face. As Silvia collected the old tray and left the room, Alice filed that little piece of information away. It would appear that the future Baron Varaldo and his kitchen maid had feelings for each other, and Alice wondered what Achille's father might have to say about that.

They continued talking and Achille gradually became more involved. It was clear from what he said that he knew little or nothing about agriculture, but Alice didn't sense any great reluctance in him at the idea of beginning to work the surrounding land a bit more. Maybe, she thought to herself, she might be able to push the decision through and the family would be able to start generating some much-needed cash. However, half an hour later when the baron himself arrived, the outlook suddenly became less hopeful. When his daughter hesitantly repeated what Alice had said about timber, milk and pork, he shook his head irritably.

'Over my dead body. We are Varaldos, not farmers.'

Alice saw Simonetta shoot a despairing glance across to her grandmother and the old lady took the hint.

'Lodovico, this is the twenty-first century and nobody owes our family any favours anymore. If you want to hold on to this land and this castle, then you're going to have to listen to what we're telling you. Otherwise, in a few years' time you might find yourself living in a scruffy apartment block on the outskirts of Parma.'

Alice suppressed a smile. Wealth was a very relative thing, but she felt sure that the next step down if the baron ever had to sell this estate would be a lot less stark than his mother was predicting. Still, if it helped to shake him out of his complacency, then more power to the old lady's elbow. She listened with interest as both his daughter and his son joined in the argument and managed to get some sort of grudging commitment from the baron that he would at least listen to whatever Alice might propose. Taking this as a positive sign, Alice asked if she could begin a formal meeting and handed around copies of the agenda she had prepared. Now that the time had come for her to start doing the job she had been engaged to do, the butterflies returned to her stomach, but she did her best to banish them. She was now the castle manager and she was determined to manage.

The meeting lasted on and off for the rest of the morning, and Alice came to the end of it feeling more relaxed and optimistic than she had done earlier. It had been agreed that she would draw up a suggested plan of action to get things moving on the conversion of the castle into a tourist attraction, but also that she would look closely into what could be done to utilise the land better. Simonetta told her that they had obtained a line of credit from their bank – using the property as a guarantee – and the baron's apprehension was clear to see. In an attempt to reassure him, Alice suggested that in the first instance she should take a look around in case there was any unused furniture and other non-essential items in the castle that might have significant value. Certainly, if they could raise most of the money for the project by selling some antiques, this would soften the blow considerably. Understandably, this suggestion was met with enthusiasm by all of them, and Alice resolved to spend the afternoon poking around.

After the meeting, Simonetta gave her two sets of keys, one for the white Fiat sitting outside in the courtyard, the other, heftier set, for the castle itself, and then led Alice on a tour of inspection.

The living accommodation extended all the way around all four sides of the central courtyard and Alice soon lost count of the number of rooms, but she did note that it took almost a quarter of an hour to complete the full circle of the courtyard and come back to where they had started. As well as an endless succession of rooms on these two floors, there were no fewer than five towers: the largest one over the main gate, and separate, smaller towers on each of the four corners of the structure.

In the gatehouse Simonetta led her up a spiral stone staircase and by the time they emerged on the roof of the tower, Alice's knee was screaming at her. She took a welcome rest as she looked out over the crenellated battlements. The 360-degree view was panoramic and they could see all the way down the valley in one direction and up to the tops of the hills in the other.

While they stood up there, Simonetta gave her the highlights of the history of the castle. 'Although the original structure was built in the early Middle Ages, it received a major makeover during the Renaissance. At that time, it was transformed from a Spartan fortress into a more comfortable family home, although it badly needs modernising now.'

Alice nodded in agreement. From what she had seen, the place still lacked quite a few modern-day creature comforts, and in a property this big, remedying that wouldn't be cheap.

Simonetta didn't show Alice the bedrooms being used by the family, but the rooms Alice did see were almost all furnished to some extent, even though most of the furniture was concealed under massive dustsheets which had probably started life white, but which were now a dull grey colour after sitting there for decades. They didn't stop to study these more closely, not least as there appeared to be a thriving population of spiders in the castle and one or two of these looked decidedly sinister. Alice had never been a spider fan and she had a feeling she was going to have some unpleasant close encounters here. Still, she told herself, a little bit of arachnophobia wasn't going to stop her making a go of it.

On the ground floor there was a vast stable and sizeable storage areas, some containing unidentifiable rusting machinery and even a couple of ancient vehicles, half-submerged beneath heaps of junk. There would be a major cleaning up job to be done, but Alice felt sure there would be ample room down here for new toilets, a cafeteria and a gift shop, as well as somewhere for administrators and guides to be based. Beneath all this, there were extensive cellars and a series of small, dank rooms that might have been dungeons back in the mists of time. Alice imagined that these could be transformed into something of interest although the family would have to be careful not to make them too scary, as there would hopefully be lots of children among the visitors.

At lunchtime she walked back down into the town to do some shopping before the general store closed for lunch. There were three or four other people in there and for a moment she even found herself checking the faces of the men in case any of them were the mysterious stranger from the previous night, but such was not the case. Giving herself a silent telling off for being so silly, she walked around the cramped confines of the little supermarket collecting food and other items she needed for her new home.

Just as she was coming out again, a battered red pickup drove past and her heart skipped a beat. She saw two figures in it, one human and one canine. Both were instantly recognisable and she had to make a concerted effort not to stop and stare moronically at them or, even worse, start waving like a mad thing. It was all over in a matter of seconds and the vehicle drove away without either of its occupants having noticed her, or, if they did, they showed no sign of it.

She wandered across the piazza towards the church and perched on a bench for a minute or two to collect herself.

What on earth was going on? On the one hand she was bemused that this man and his admittedly adorable dog could reduce her to the state of a giddy teenager, but her more pragmatic self did her best to point out the upside to this. Could it really be that she was finally beginning to emerge from the protective cocoon she had spun around herself since the accident? Wendy, the counsellor she had been seeing on and off for the last four years, would no doubt approve. Maybe she should send Wendy a text.

Pulling herself together, she made a visit to the bakers where she bought a big loaf of bread and a little strawberry tart as a first-day treat, and then she went back to her new apartment and made herself lunch. As she was eating a ham and cheese sandwich, her phone rang; it was her mum, checking to see how her first morning had gone.

Alice passed on the good news that everything had gone better than she had hoped, and that she had got the impression that all of them, including the baron himself, were prepared to go through with the project of opening up to the public, however unwillingly. She then went on to talk about her plan to start making the vast expanse of land generate some income, and her mum handed the phone to her dad, who immediately offered help.

'Hello, sweetheart, I've been thinking about what you said about the land up there and I've got a few ideas for you. First, what about timber?'

'Already thought of that, Dad. Any other ideas? How about sheep?'

'Not sheep, they're more trouble than they're worth.' He gave a snort. 'They are immensely stupid animals and in my experience they spend all of their lives trying to find ways of killing themselves, whether it's by getting stuck in hedges, falling over on their backs and being unable to get up again, or catching one of the many diseases that affect sheep. No, I think what you should think about is alpacas.'

'Alpacas?' Alice certainly hadn't thought of this.

'Definitely. They're no trouble to look after. They're hardy hill animals and apparently you can make good money by selling their fleeces, and their meat as well I believe. Build up a herd of a few hundred – you've got bags of land there – and you start making a profit. I'm seriously thinking about replacing these damn ostriches with alpacas. That's the other good thing about alpacas compared to ostriches: they're very placid animals and they don't try to kick or peck you to death when they're feeling moody.'

This sounded like an excellent idea, and Alice added *alpacas* beneath *cattle* and *horses* to the list she had started to compile. On her father's advice she scrubbed out *sheep* and, on reflection, she also drew a line through *pigs*. Although potentially profitable, they could easily create a blot on the landscape and for an estate trying to lure in tourists, it was probably better to stick with photogenic animals.

She went back up to the castle at two o'clock and spent the afternoon ferreting around all the rooms, checking under dust sheets and moving piles of rubbish, to see if she could find anything of reasonable value for resale. Her hunt produced mixed results. As expected, she ran into a scary selection of eight-legged arthropods, several of which looked positively lethal, but she persevered all the same. Apart from the spiders, there were some very nice pieces of furniture, particularly a large, sculpted dresser which would no doubt fetch a decent price at auction, but nothing she saw looked likely to raise anything like the substantial amounts that were going to be needed for the conversion of the castle. The problem was that these very items were the kind of thing that it would be good to have on display when the castle opened its doors to the public. They could hardly expect people to walk through empty room after empty room.

Knowing she was going to need an office, she decided that the ground floor of the main tower and the gatehouse could be reserved for the administration, including an office for herself. After poking about in the shadows with the aid of the torch on her phone (there was no electricity in this part of the castle) she identified a suitable room for her office, from where she would be able to keep an eye on what would become the reception area. First, it would need to be thoroughly cleaned and disinfected and some effective mouse and rat traps installed. From the size of the droppings all over the floor, there appeared to be a thriving colony of them in here, and she had no intention of sharing her office with the local rodent population, not to mention all manner of scary spiders.

In the course of her tour, she went into the kitchen and sat down for a chat with Ines and her daughter and gratefully accepted the offer of a cup of coffee and a home-made biscuit. Silvia didn't say much but Alice was struck yet again by how outstandingly beautiful she was. She could have been on the front cover of a fashion magazine, so why on earth was she working as a kitchen maid?

Ines volunteered the information that she was sixty-two and had worked for the family since the age of sixteen. Her husband had also worked here in the castle but had sadly died of lung cancer when he was still only in his fifties. With a bit of coaxing from Alice she came up with a bit more background on the history of the place and, in particular, the underlying feud with the Montorso family. According to her father, who had also spent his whole life working at the castle, the origin of the bitter dispute went back to medieval times when the two families had ended up on opposite sides in the vicious internecine wars between the Guelphs and the Ghibellines. According to her father, relations between the families had gradually improved over the centuries until the early twentieth century but had taken another hit with the advent of fascism in Italy.

Here again they had ended up on different sides. The Montorso family had proved to be staunch supporters of Mussolini and his Blackshirts while the Varaldo family had opposed what was happening and had suffered persecution as a result. Simonetta's grandfather had even been imprisoned for some months shortly before the Italian capitulation in 1943, managing to get out of jail during the brief hiatus before the German occupying forces took over. Alice resolved to try to sit down with the baroness sometime in the hope of hearing more about what had happened during the war. This story showed that the strained relations between the two families were more recent and so more relatable.

Ines told her that there were only two full-time members of staff here at the castle apart from herself and Silvia, and apparently they didn't do much apart from general maintenance and a certain amount of work in the grounds, looking after a handful of chickens and a small vegetable garden. From the look of disapproval on her face, which was shared by her daughter, it was clear that the kitchen staff didn't have a very high opinion of the work ethic of the ground staff, Alfonso and Pietro.

It was beginning to get late by this time, but Alice resolved to go and seek out these two gentlemen the following morning to ascertain just exactly what their duties entailed. She had no reason to doubt Ines's version, but out of fairness she needed to see for herself.

Chapter 9

The next day proved to be unexpectedly interesting. After checking with Simonetta to ask where she might find Pietro and Alfonso, Alice spent half an hour tramping through the surrounding fields and woods until she finally came across the two men. It had rained in the night but she had come well equipped and her boots kept her dry as she picked her way through the mud and the long grass. She brought her stick with her just in case but she managed to negotiate the terrain without needing it. Finally she came out onto a rough track and happened upon a sweet little stone cottage that could have come straight out of Hansel and Gretel. It was at the edge of a forest made up of mature conifers and deciduous trees which, to her eyes, were just crying out to be harvested, and there were wisps of smoke coming out of the chimney. Parked outside the cottage was a vintage tractor which probably belonged in a museum. It was so old, it looked as though the tyres were solid rubber. She shuddered to think how bone rattlingly uncomfortable it would be to ride on something like this along the rutted, potholed track.

She walked up to the door, propped her stick out of the way off to one side and knocked twice. There was the sound of a chair being pushed back, followed by footsteps coming to the door, which opened with a creak. Alice hadn't been told anything about either Alfonso or Pietro and she had somehow been expecting a couple of old men of a similar vintage to the tractor parked outside. In consequence, she was surprised to find herself confronted by a man with an unruly mass of ginger hair who looked younger than she was. He was also over a foot taller and a foot wider than she was and he actually had to tilt his head to one side to avoid hitting the door frame. Feeling some-what intimidated, Alice nevertheless managed to summon a bright smile and held out her hand, but not without a certain amount of trepidation.

'Good morning, my name's Alice and I'm the new castle manager.'

She distinctly saw his jaw drop and she felt his eyes staring down at her in disbelief. A voice from behind him made him half turn but he appeared incapable of speech.

'Who is it, Pietro?'

Seeing that the giant was still looking stunned, Alice raised her voice and repeated what she had just said and she heard hurried footsteps approaching from within. A man of about fifty appeared behind Pietro and elbowed him out of the way so that he could shake Alice's hand.

'Signora, good morning, I'm very pleased to meet you. We both are, aren't we, Pietro?'

He jabbed his elbow into the big man's side again and this finally did the trick. Pietro extended a massive paw and shook Alice's hand remarkably gently, murmuring, '*Buongiorno*, signora.'

'Come in, signora. Can we offer you a cup of coffee? We're just on our morning break.'

Alice walked inside and looked around. The interior of the cottage was, if anything, even sweeter than the outside and she felt sure that there would be a place for this magical little construction when children started visiting the property. There was an appetising smell of coffee in the room and this had presumably been made on the old-fashioned stove sitting alongside an antique workbench, behind which was a rack of even older-looking tools. Some of these were so antiquated she had no idea what purpose they might have served. She glanced across towards the older man and nodded.

'I'd love a cup of coffee, thank you. I assume you're Alfonso, is that right?'

'Yes, signora, and this is my son, Pietro. Pietro, pour the lady some coffee. See if you can find a clean cup. Would you like to sit down, signora?'

Alice was getting a bit fed up with being called 'signora' so she thought she'd better spell things out to the two of them. 'My name's Alice and there's no need to call me signora. I'm just an employee, the same as you two.' She sat down on an old three-legged stool slightly apprehensively but, apart from creaking, it seemed sturdy enough and the immediate relief to her aching knee almost made her sigh with pleasure. 'I only started work here yesterday and I'm just taking a look around the castle and the grounds, trying to get an idea of what's where and meeting everybody who works here. I wonder if you could tell me what you two do exactly.'

To her surprise, Alfonso said almost exactly what Ines had said about the two of them. 'Not very much, I'm afraid. We look after the chickens and we grow vegetables for the kitchen. We clear the snow in winter, do a bit of painting and decorating, but every time I suggest something more adventurous, the baron shoots it down.' He shook his head ruefully. 'He doesn't like change.' He lowered his voice. 'And since his wife died a couple of years ago, it's been hard even to get to see him. He's just not interested.'

This assessment of Baron Lodovico came as no surprise to Alice from what she had already seen and heard, and she began to take a liking to Alfonso. She appreciated his apparent honesty and decided to run some of her ideas across him to see what he and his son thought of them. She waited until Pietro had brought her a steaming cup of coffee – the cup itself not exactly sparkling clean, but she hoped the boiling hot liquid would kill off anything too sinister – before embarking on her plans for the future. As she talked to the two men, she was encouraged to see genuine enthusiasm on both faces. This came as a relief. She had come to look for them half-expecting to find a couple of lazy shirkers, but this didn't appear to be the case. It sounded as if it wasn't that they hadn't wanted to work, but that the baron hadn't allowed them to work. She mentioned growing crops and rearing livestock without specifying at this stage what she had in mind and she was heartened by Alfonso's response.

'Excellent idea. Simonetta told us months ago that she wanted to open the castle to the public, but we really didn't believe for a moment that the baron would go through with it, did we, Pietro?'

The giant nodded but said nothing. He still appeared to be trying to get his head around the fact that there was now a castle manager, and that she was a woman. Clearly he was a man of very few words but he looked friendly enough, which was just as well, considering his size. It didn't seem to matter; his father appeared more than happy to make up for his son's silence.

'This is music to my ears, Sig— Alees. If you don't mind me asking, your accent isn't from around here. Can I ask where you're from?'

'I'm English, but I spent a number of years living up north in the Dolomites.'

'Ah, so that's it. From your accent I thought you might be from Venice. Anyway, you're absolutely right, the estate's crying out to be farmed. We have hundreds of hectares of woodland here just dying to be worked, and the price of timber has gone up so much in recent months. There's a sawmill a bit further down the valley and I'm sure you could do a deal with them very easily. Otherwise, if you want my opinion, it's cows that we need. My cousin up the valley makes parmesan cheese – his dairy produces DOP parmesan – and I know he'd be only too pleased to buy milk from us. The air up here's clean; the pasture's rich and lush. It's crying out for cows.'

'DOP? Sorry, I'm not familiar with that.'

'Protected Denomination of Origin. It means he makes *authentic* parmesan, Parmigiano Reggiano. It's only in a very specific area that you can get a DOP and it's a guarantee of quality.'

This sounded promising. Alice gave him a smile. 'Cows sound like a great idea. Now all I've got to do is to convince the baron. Wish me luck.'

As she drank her cloudy coffee, trying not to think too hard about what might be lurking below the surface, she chatted with them and she learned that Alfonso had been working here for over thirty years and Pietro for seven.

She cautiously brought up the subject of the Montorso family and the ongoing feud, and she saw Alfonso shake his head in disbelief.

'It's been going on for centuries, but as far as most of us in the town are concerned, the responsibility for it still continuing today lies with the mayor. What's in the past should stay in the past, but Cesare's a nasty piece of work and he won't let it go. The only reason he got elected mayor was because nobody else wanted to stand against him. One man tried, and all the glass in his greenhouse was mysteriously smashed a week later. No, Cesare Montorso's a bad lot.'

'You're saying he actually resorted to violence?' Alice was horrified.

'It was never proved but, for my money, Cesare was behind it, even if he didn't actually do it himself. My big brother, Daniele, went to school with him and he says the man was a bully even then.' He looked across towards Alice. 'He's even fallen out with his own family. One of his sons went off and left home as soon as he could and then his wife left him a few years ago. Like I say, he's a bad lot.'

Alice sat back and digested what she had just heard. It didn't sound as though there was going to be much chance of reconciliation between the two families if the leader of the opposing family was such a brute. Still, she told herself, that was the situation and she knew she had to accept it and work around it – if she could. She asked Alfonso to tell her exactly where Varaldo territory started and finished and he gave her a detailed outline. After drinking the last of her coffee and doing her best to ignore the couple of amorphous dark lumps at the bottom – dead flies maybe?

– she left them and carried on with her walking tour of the estate. Following Alfonso's instructions, she set off along a track that snaked upwards through the trees, climbing steadily for almost half an hour until she emerged onto a rocky promontory from where he had told her she would be able to survey the full extent of the baron's lands.

She sat down on a windblown boulder and took a breather. If her knee had been protesting before, it was positively screaming now, but she didn't mind. It had got her up here and she was mildly surprised. Maybe the mountain air was helping in some way.

She sat there and reflected on her first couple of days here at the castle. The sheer scale of the work ahead had been worrying her ever since the job offer, but she now felt a growing optimism that she would be up to the task and that the results would be spectacular. On a personal level, the hesitation she had experienced at the thought of returning to Italy and the unpleasant memories this might stir up inside her was gradually being replaced by a confidence that had been lacking in her for years now. Above all, the spectre of Maurizio returning to haunt her psyche had retreated. Whether this had anything to do with the unexpected feelings aroused in her by her mystery man remained to be seen.

She was perspiring freely after the climb, but the view from up here was definitely worth the effort. She was now looking down onto the whole valley from where it started high up in the hills to the right of her to where it joined the main valley ten kilometres below in the opposite direction. The castle on its little rise was laid out before her like a model, and she could even see a tiny figure in the courtyard – presumably Ines or her daughter

– hanging out the washing on a line. Beyond the castle was the town and on the opposite side of the valley was the Montorso family farm. She swivelled her head around and looked up at the hillside that continued to climb behind her. The forest ended abruptly a little way further up and the terrain became open grassland.

She would need a detailed map of the area but Alfonso had told her that all of this side of the valley, right up to the ridge high above her, belonged to the family and extended in both directions almost as far as the eye could see. From her vantage point she did a rough calculation and worked out that approximately half of Varaldo land was heavily wooded – mainly, but not exclusively, with conifers – and the other half was lush green pasture. Certainly, there was plenty of room for a good-sized herd of cows and even alpacas as well. Her eye was drawn to a smaller property near the road a kilometre or so down the valley. In the fields around this she could clearly see horses and she resolved to take a trip down there at the weekend to see if there was any chance of a ride. Growing up, she had had her own pony and since the accident she had returned to riding as a great way to get out in the fresh air. She felt sure that the best way to survey the terrain around here would be on horseback.

That afternoon she sat down with Simonetta in one of the many rooms in the castle – this one a magnificent library with probably thousands of books on floor-to-ceiling shelves all around the walls. It occurred to her as she sat down and looked around that there might be valuable first editions among these, so she added 'book expert' alongside 'antiques expert' to her To Do List. She took Simonetta through her initial list of recommendations and between them they drew up a document for presentation to the rest of the family, hopefully for their approval. Apart from a number of practical bureaucratic matters relating to the conversion of the castle into a tourist attraction, they also listed forestry and agriculture, specifically cows and, after a bit of discussion, they added alpacas to the list.

Alice also suggested a riding stable, but Simonetta shook her head. 'There's already a stable just outside of town and it's run by a good friend of mine, so I wouldn't want to intrude on her business.'

Alice explained that she had been riding since she was three and it turned out that Simonetta, too, was passionate about horses. Pulling out her phone, she glanced across at Alice. 'Have you any plans for this evening? Fancy a ride?' Alice nodded eagerly and Simonetta dialled a number. 'I'll call Emilia now; she owns the stables. It's light until quite late, so we could have a couple of hours and I'll be able to show you more of the estate. Five o'clock okay with you?'

'That sounds perfect.'

Chapter 10

Alice went home to change at half-past four, thanking the instinct that had made her pack her riding clothes. Simonetta picked her up in the Land Rover and they made the short journey down to the stables. Emilia was a friendly but no-nonsense sort of woman, probably in her fifties, who bore an uncanny resemblance to Daphne who ran the stable at the manor back in Devon. Ten minutes later Alice was on a handsome bay called Horace – well, Orazio really – and she and Simonetta were on their way. To Alice's surprise, Simonetta headed up the far side of the valley opposite the castle. As they walked their horses up a stony track, she explained why she had brought Alice over here.

'From this side of the valley we get a really good view of all our land and you can point out to me where you think the best areas would be for crops and for livestock.'

At the far end of a field to the right of them, Alice briefly caught sight of a figure on foot. Although he was only visible for a matter of seconds and too far away for her to make out facial features, what was clear was that he was a tall man with fair hair and broad shoulders. At his side was a black dog – and from here it looked very much like a Labrador. As they disappeared from sight behind a thick clump of trees, Alice found herself questioning whether she really had seen the two of them, or whether this had been some weird trick of her imagination. She was giving herself a silent talking-to when Simonetta turned towards her, and the expression on her face was one of embarrassment, guilt even.

'Alice, would you mind if I met you up at the top? I've just seen a friend of mine and I'd like to pop across for a quick chat.'

Alice was quick to agree and they arranged to meet at the point where the track emerged from the fields onto open grassland, probably half a mile above them or so. Horace the horse carried on picking his way stolidly up the track while Alice found herself wondering about that guilty expression she had spotted on Simonetta's face. Was this because the man was somebody that Alice shouldn't have seen? Were Simonetta and this man in some sort of romantic relationship even? But if this were the case, Alice asked herself, why should this be a problem? Was there something here that people weren't supposed to know? Was he somebody else's husband, for instance?

While Simonetta spurred her horse into a canter and headed across the field towards the clump of trees where the man and his dog had disappeared, Alice and Horace continued their leisurely walk up the track. This gradually curved around the top of the field, and a few hundred yards further on she distinctly saw Simonetta rein in her horse and climb off. That same man emerged from the trees and, while his dog jumped excitedly at Simonetta to be petted, the man enveloped her in his arms, and Alice saw them entwined in a loving embrace.

Two things were immediately clear: the man was unmistakably the same man she had seen in the restaurant and, just as clearly, Simonetta was in love with him, or at least very fond of him. And he appeared to feel the same way about her. Even his dog appeared to share his feelings.

To the accompaniment of the gentle clip-clop of Horace's hooves, Alice gradually tried to make sense of what she had just seen. This discovery automatically removed the mystery man from her own life and by so doing should stop her from fantasising about him. Besides, Simonetta was her boss and, apart from the fact that Alice felt she was developing a real friendship with her, she wasn't the type of woman to intrude on another woman's relationship, even if a good-looking man like that turned out to be attracted to her. So this meant that this man who had so mysteriously fascinated her was now forever out of her reach.

But that was probably for the best, wasn't it?

To her surprise, she felt considerable disappointment at the thought that he had now been removed from her life – without ever really being in it in the first place, if she was honest. She did her best to be positive and to tell herself once more that he had served a valuable purpose in making her realise that maybe the time had come for her to try to overcome the pall of insecurity that had swamped her since the accident and consider looking for a man for herself. As she surreptitiously watched the happy couple until they were masked from sight by more trees, she told herself she was happy for the two of them, but she couldn't help a feeling of regret at what might have been. Still, as her dad so often said, there was no point crying over spilt milk.

'Come on, Horace. Let's get a move on, shall we?' In case he didn't understand English, she gave him a prod with her heels and he obediently broke into a trot.

Fifteen minutes later they came out onto the open grassland and Alice slowed to give Horace a rest. While he reached down to help himself to some of the lush green grass at the side of the vestigial path, she swivelled around in the saddle and looked back down the hillside. It looked like the track she had been following had probably been skirting around fields belonging to the mayor and his family. His red brick farmhouse with its outbuildings was now almost directly below her and she could see that it was a sizeable property. A herd of fifty or sixty cows in a field near the farm were being brought in for milking and she could hear the barking of a sheepdog as it rounded them up. Standing by the gate was a man. It was impossible to tell from this distance, but it looked like an older man, maybe the mayor himself. And Simonetta's friend, the man with the Labrador? He, too, had been on Montorso land; could it be he was something to do with the Montorso family? That might explain the guilt on Simonetta's face. Alice smiled to herself. All very Shakespearean.

The sound of hooves attracted her attention and she looked back to see Simonetta trotting briskly up the hill towards her. When she came to a halt alongside Alice, she was looking flushed, but whether that was as a result of the vigorous ride or her recent romantic encounter remained to be seen. Although Alice was intrigued, she knew that her employer's personal life was no business of hers and so she resisted the urge to ask. As it turned out, she didn't need to, because Simonetta had already decided to take her into her confidence.

'Alice, can I ask you to keep a secret please, a big secret, a really big secret?'

'Of course. I won't tell a soul. What is it?'

Simonetta took a few moments to find the right words. 'My friend back there, the man I've just been talking to, is Tommaso Montorso.' She looked across at Alice and immediately saw that Alice had understood the implications of this information. 'That's right, his father's the mayor, and his family and our family have been fighting for centuries. If his father saw me with him, he'd have a fit. I don't know what he'd do, but he's capable of anything.'

Alice reached over and gripped Simonetta's arm for a moment, giving it an encouraging squeeze. 'I was wondering if it might be something like that and I was just telling myself it sounded like something Shakespeare might have written.' For obvious reasons, she didn't attempt to liken Simonetta's situation to that of Romeo and Juliet – after all, in that play both characters died.

Simonetta nodded miserably. 'I know it sounds crazy in the twenty-first century and I'm sure you must find it incredible, but I'm in in such a terrible situation. Tommaso and I have known each other for years and I fell hopelessly in love with him ages ago. While I was working down in Parma it was OK. He and I spent most weekends together and nobody up here needed to know anything about it, but since I've moved back here after my mother's death, we've had to be incredibly careful. Like I say, if Tommi's father were to find out, it could end really badly.'

'What about *your* father? How do you think he would react… if you don't mind me asking?'

'Papà would be shocked but, deep down, I know he'd want me to be happy.' She shook her head regretfully. 'But the problem isn't with *my* father.'

'And I suppose now, with all the work that's going to be happening at the castle, you can't just go off and elope. I see the problem. You're stuck, aren't you?'

'I'm afraid I am – at least for now. I honestly don't know how to get out of it and Tommi's in a similar situation. He's been running the farm for years now while his father's been getting more and more involved with local politics. His mother couldn't stand living with his father anymore and left him a few years ago, but Tommi felt he couldn't just abandon the farm and run off to South America or somewhere with me, even if I could get away. Without him, their farm would grind to a halt and he has all the animals to consider, but more than that, he feels he has to stay to keep an eye on his father.'

'In what way?'

'Neither of us is a psychiatrist, but Tommi's convinced his father's suffering from some sort of progressive, deteriorating neurological illness. He says his father wakes up screaming in the night and his outbursts of anger and violence – he's always been like that – are getting more serious and more frequent. Tommi feels he has to stick with him for his father's sake and for the sake of the people around him, both at the farm and in the town, for fear that he'll do something awful.'

'How terrible for him… and for you.'

'I know.' Simonetta wiped the back of her hand across her eyes and took a couple of deep breaths. 'So Tommi and I are stuck having to tiptoe about like a couple of criminals, always waiting for somebody to see us together and tell his father. It's like having the sword of Damocles hanging over our heads.'

'That's absolutely dreadful.' Alice reached over and gave her another comforting pat on the arm. 'Anyway, look, thank you for telling me this, and if I can help out in any way, maybe by providing an alibi or something, don't hesitate. I'm touched that you've trusted me with this news and I promise I won't breathe a word to anybody.'

'Thanks, Alice, that means a lot. I felt sure I could trust you and, to be honest, I just had to tell somebody. It's been driving me crazy and of course, there's nobody here I can talk to safely. I have lots of friends in the town, but I don't dare take the risk of telling anybody local. Even in Parma hardly anybody knows about us. Tommi and I are forced to sneak around and we just can't tell a soul.'

'Not even your brother?'

'Oh, Lord, no. I know he'd understand and he'd be very supportive, but ever since he was a little boy he's been pathologically incapable of keeping a secret for more than a few hours. If I were to tell him, I know it would be all around the town by the end of the week.' Simonetta summoned a weak smile. 'Sorry to bother you with all my woes, but I just had to speak to somebody before I exploded.'

'Well, just use me as a way of letting off steam. Like I say, anything you tell me won't go any further.'

'Thanks, Alice, you don't know how much that means to me.' Simonetta took another deep breath. 'Now, I think it's time you and I went for a proper ride. First one to the shepherd's hut up there?'

Chapter 11

The rest of the week passed quickly, and by the weekend Alice was beginning to build up a picture of what needed to be done. All she had to do now was to convince the Varaldo family, and the baron in particular, that she was right. Together with Simonetta, she drew up comprehensive proposals for the conversion of the castle into a tourist attraction and for more profitable use of the land. They gradually refined the plans until she was able to prepare the agenda for a meeting to take place at ten o'clock on Monday morning with all the family present. As the days went by, her relationship with Simonetta grew ever closer and they chatted together about all sorts of things as well but, by tacit mutual agreement, Tommaso Montorso was not mentioned again by either of them.

Alice went riding on her own on Sunday afternoon and took Horace the horse – for whom she was developing considerable affection – on a leisurely tour of the Varaldo estate. She had managed to get hold of a fairly detailed local map at the general store run by her landlady's friend, Vincenzo, and this allowed her to navigate her way around fields, woods and open grassland without too much trouble.

She admired the scenery as Horace plodded up narrow tracks and across open fields knee-deep in grass, and she realised that she was beginning to feel very comfortable here in the valley. The dusting of snow she had noted when she first came here on the tops of the far distant hills had disappeared without trace and as the month of June dawned the temperature began to rise noticeably. She was starting to get her bearings around the estate and was increasingly familiar with the outside and the inside of the castle, from the moat to the battlements. She had already decided where she hoped to create a reception area and an office for herself – in what used to be the guardroom by the entrance – and the first thing she intended to do if she managed to get full approval at Monday's meeting would be to contact an architect specialising in old buildings and a good electrician. One of the things she would be telling the family would be to brace themselves for some hefty expense in bringing the infrastructure up to standard.

As she and Horace wandered around the estate, she also spent a lot of time thinking about the situation in which Simonetta now found herself. It really was scarcely believable in this day and age that such ancient rivalries should persist, and she felt genuinely sorry for both Simonetta and Tommaso. His father sounded mentally unstable to put it mildly, and she found herself thinking how awful it must be for a son to be afraid of his father and for a wife to be driven to the point of leaving home by her husband's behaviour. Come to think of it, hadn't Alfonso the groundsman told her that another son had gone off and left after quarrelling with the father? She sincerely hoped that things would work out for Simonetta, particularly as it sounded as if Tommaso's father was getting progressively worse. At some point, she was going to have to go to the town hall where in all likelihood she would meet him. She wasn't looking forward to it one bit.

Soberly, she reflected about the weird coincidence of how Tommaso Montorso had not only found his way into Simonetta's heart but had also made such an impression upon her. Of course he was now forbidden fruit but she couldn't help a lingering feeling of regret for what might have been. Still, she kept telling herself, the fact that any man had made such an impression on her had to be a sign that she was beginning to put the past behind her. At least, that was what she hoped.

That evening she decided to go to the Casa Rosa for dinner again. It had started raining just as she came back from her ride, and when she left the house for the restaurant at seven-thirty, the sky was a deep grey all over and it was almost dark, in spite of sunset not normally being for at least another hour or more. The rain was coming down harder and harder now and she was glad of her waterproof boots and her big umbrella. When she reached the restaurant she left the umbrella in a bucket by the door and as she walked in, doing her best not to limp too badly as the damp air got to her knee, she found herself automatically scanning the tables for her mystery man, now revealed as Tommaso Montorso, and in consequence off limits. There was no sign of him, and although she knew full well that he belonged to Simonetta, a momentary pang of disappointment shot through her when she saw the table in the corner lying empty.

She received a friendly greeting from the same waiter as the previous week. Recognising her from last Sunday, he stopped to chat, and she learned that his name was Roberto and that he had lived in the town all his life.

When she told him about her new position at the castle he looked interested; so interested, in fact, that he must have told the proprietor, who came out a minute later with a bottle of Lambrusco and two glasses to welcome her to the town. He was a man probably in his late sixties with snow white hair. He introduced himself as Giorgio, and Alice remembered Luisella telling her that his son was now the head chef. He was quite obviously on the hunt for more information and she soon realised why he was so interested. He wanted to know whether the castle would represent competition for his business. Alice was quick to offer reassurance.

'Hopefully, this will put Varaldo on the map. I was delighted to see that you're a hotel as well as a restaurant and I'm sure having the castle as a tourist attraction should bring you a lot of extra business. We're planning to have a coffee shop up at the castle, but there's no question of a full restaurant, so it should be a win-win situation for you.'

The restaurateur looked delighted and relieved, and they chatted amicably for several minutes before he stood up and told her he had to get back to see how things were going in the kitchen. Although Alice protested weakly, he insisted on leaving her the bottle of Lambrusco and she did her best not to drink all of it in the course of what was another excellent meal. She had only ever had Lambrusco a few times before in her life and had generally found it sickly sweet and far too fizzy. This wine, however, was a deep dark red in colour and neither too sweet, nor too fizzy. Still, good as it was, she decided not to follow her instincts and risk getting plastered. This time the meal consisted of lamb stew with polenta, followed by home-made cherry tart with amazing meringue ice cream.

She called her mum for a chat but made no mention of the revelations she had received from Simonetta about the love of her life. She told her mum and dad all about her plans for the castle and asked them to keep their fingers crossed in the morning that the family would approve her proposals. Finally, at just after nine she finished her coffee and went over to the counter to thank Giorgio and pay the bill.

She was just retrieving her umbrella from the bucket by the door when she felt a particularly intimate poke on her bottom and spun around to discover that her aggressor was none other than a black Labrador with a broad canine smile on its face. Behind him, walking towards her and looking apologetic, was none other than Tommaso Montorso. He reached down and caught hold of the dog by the collar, yanking him backwards.

'Frank, come here and leave the lady alone.' He looked up from the unrepentant dog who was wagging his tail enthusiastically. 'I'm very sorry. He's still young and he's a bit too friendly.' He spoke Italian with an educated accent and she found no difficulty in understanding him.

Alice gave him a smile in return and bent down to stroke the dog. For a moment she even considered mentioning to his master that she had seen him in the fields the other day, but, remembering her vow of silence to Simonetta, she allowed no sign of recognition to show on her face and stuck to trivia. Maybe it was because she now knew he was off limits, but she found it remarkably easy to talk to him without the usual awkwardness around good-looking men that had blighted her life ever since her accident. 'That's perfectly all right. I love Labradors; we always had one at home. I'm pleased to feel that his fur's dry. Hopefully, that means the rain's stopped.'

'Yes, it stopped about half an hour ago.' For a moment it looked as though he was on the point of saying more but then he lapsed into silence. A little thrill of triumph went through her. Could it be that he was more nervous about speaking to her than she was? Progress indeed! She found it very easy to give him another smile.

'That's good. Well, goodnight to you both.'

'Good night. Come on, Frank, let's go and eat.'

She turned away to hide a little smile as she reflected that their choice of conversation, in spite of being in Italian, had been almost Anglo-Saxon: the weather, always a safe topic for strangers. As she walked out into the fresh night air she couldn't help reflecting that he had given his dog an English name. Curious. But more curious – and concerning – was the undeniable fact that when she had seen him, her heart had done another little somersault. Considering what she now knew about him and Simonetta, this was the last thing she needed.

–

The meeting on Monday morning lasted for almost three hours. Alice started with the plans she and Simonetta had concocted for the thousands of acres of land surrounding the castle. Grudgingly, the baron allowed himself to be persuaded to go along with the idea of trying to do a deal with the local sawmill and begin to harvest some of the thousands of trees and to replace them with saplings. Alice was keen to point out that this would be done in a sustainable way. The main stumbling block was her plan to introduce livestock and to cultivate at least some of the fields so as to provide winter feed and bedding for the animals. The baron rambled on grumpily about tradition, history, and family values, but without any attempt to be pragmatic and accept the situation in which the family now found itself. In the end it was his mother who cut across her son's protests and spoke to him in a voice that brooked no argument.

'Lodovico, we have to do this. It's not a question of whether you *want* to or not. If we don't start generating some money, we risk losing everything, including this castle. It's all very well talking about tradition, but times change and sometimes you have to take hard decisions. I know your father would have agreed with Alice's plan. He spoke about doing something similar himself on a number of occasions.'

This finally got through to the baron and he looked across at his mother in surprise. 'Is that true? Did father really say that?'

A less confrontational expression appeared on the face of the old baroness. 'Yes, he did, my dear, and I know he would want you to agree to this plan.'

After this intervention, the baron had no option but to admit defeat and he reluctantly gave them his agreement. Alice heaved a quiet sigh of relief and moved the meeting on to her ideas for the castle itself. She gradually led them through the different items she had listed in order to turn the castle into a tourist attraction. She made a point of emphasising the considerable costs that would be involved, as she didn't want them to have any unwelcome surprises.

Although it took time, she steadily managed to get agreement on everything, starting with an urgent survey by a good architect, preferably one specialising in historic properties. Once they had the architect's recommendations, she would move on to getting estimates from builders, decorators, electricians and plumbers and at the same time she would set about applying to the heritage authorities for the all-important planning permission and authorisation to proceed.

She also proposed transforming the storerooms and stables on the ground floor of the castle into a cafeteria, a gift shop, and her latest idea, designed to appeal to the baron: a museum of the Varaldo family. This at least was greeted with his enthusiastic approval, as Alice had hoped it would, and he even started smiling at the thought of his very own museum. Finally she came on to the last item on the agenda which she felt sure would prove to be the most contentious of all: where the family would live.

'As I'm sure you've realised by now, opening your home to the public is going to mean considerable intrusion into your privacy. Obviously there's no way you would want visitors wandering in and out of your living space, so I have a rather radical suggestion for you.' She paused for breath and then laid out her proposal, realising as she did so that she was actually crossing her fingers out of sight by her side. With her free hand she waved around at the walls and ceiling of the living room. 'As these rooms here are the most impressive of the whole building, I would suggest that they be among those opened to the public. Doing this will mean considerable upheaval for you but, in order to preserve your privacy, my proposal is that you consider moving into the towers. There are five of them. If we exclude the tower by the main gate, that leaves four. They all offer a lot of living space over three floors. How would you feel about it?'

The baron stared at her. 'You mean move out of here? But I've lived here all my life. Besides, what about the kitchens and the bedrooms and that sort of thing?'

Alice had talked this over with Simonetta earlier and she was pleased to let her take over. 'The thing is, Papà, we can't keep using these rooms if they're open to the public. The beauty of Alice's idea of using the towers is that they can be easily locked off and kept completely separate from any visitors. That way we should be able to stay private while at the same time opening the main rooms of the castle to the public. How we decide to divide the accommodation can be worked out later; maybe one tower for general living space and then other towers for sleeping, or one tower for you and one tower for Nonna and so on, or whatever you prefer.'

To Alice's surprise, and relief, it was Simonetta's grandmother who then chimed in on their side. 'I think that's a marvellous idea. I've been wondering about living arrangements. I must confess I even had a dream the other night in which I was lying in bed and the door to my bedroom suddenly opened. Two foreign tourists came in jabbering away in a strange language and started taking photographs of me in my nightdress. The idea of being able to close myself off in one of the towers and lock the door seems an excellent solution.'

Alice was then delighted to hear Simonetta's brother agree with his grandmother. 'Four towers, four of us, it makes a lot of sense.' Achille turned to his father. 'What do you think, Papà? Don't you agree it's the best solution?'

A hush descended on the room and all eyes were on the baron. Alice was already rehearsing a counter argument to the objection she felt sure he was about to produce, when he looked up and, to her surprise, and probably to the surprise of everybody else in the room, a smile appeared on his face.

'I think that's an excellent idea. As you all know, I've never been in favour of the idea of opening the castle to strangers, and one of my main concerns all along has been the intrusion upon our privacy this would cause. The idea of the towers resolves that beautifully.' For the very first time since Alice had known him, he looked directly at her and addressed her by name. 'Well done, Alice. A really good solution to a problem that's been troubling me greatly.'

Unexpected praise from such an unlikely source produced the urge in Alice to jump to her feet and run across and hug him, but she restrained the impulse and just beamed back at him. She asked if anybody had any suggestions about architects but none could recommend anybody in particular so she resolved to cast her net wider that afternoon.

Chapter 12

There were no fewer than eighteen architects listed on the Internet as having offices in Parma, many claiming to have experience of historical properties, and she studied them closely, knowing how important the right choice would be. As she did so, she remembered seeing the parish church in one of the villages she had passed on her way here swathed in scaffolding, so she jumped into her Fiat and drove down there to ask if they could recommend their architect. On the way, she passed the sawmill that Alfonso had mentioned and decided to strike while the iron was hot. She pulled in through the gates and parked between two massive trucks loaded with tree trunks. A sign on the wall told her that the sawmill belonged to Rocco Emiliano and an arrow on the wall in front of her pointed the way to the *Ufficio* so she headed for it.

The office was up a short flight of steps and occupied the end of a long building within which she could hear the unmistakable sound of an electric saw working. Inside the cramped room she found a powerfully built man with a neck tattoo and a ferocious pair of sideburns. He looked like Wolverine from the X-Men and she had a feeling this was probably deliberate, not least as he was wearing a faded T-shirt which had started life with a now barely distinguishable Superman logo on it. This particular superhero was sitting behind a desk absolutely covered in paperwork.

'Good afternoon, how can I help?' He sounded friendly enough, so she took heart.

'I was wondering if you might be interested in buying some timber.'

'How much timber?' He sounded dismissive. 'We're really only interested in large quantities.'

'And what would constitute a large quantity for you? As a rough estimate, we have four or five hundred hectares of partly coniferous, partly deciduous, woodland. Is that the sort of thing you'd be interested in?' She had to resist the urge to laugh out loud at the expression that appeared on his face. He looked genuinely gobsmacked.

'Did you say five *hundred* hectares? Are you sure?'

She took pity on him, introduced herself and explained who she was and where she was now working. His reaction was enthusiastic. He waved her into a seat and picked up the phone with his left hand while offering her his right to shake. 'My name's Rocco Emiliano, I'm very pleased to meet you. Can I offer you a coffee?' Seeing her nod, he shouted into the phone. 'Stella, two coffees, please. We have a visitor... and see if you can find some biscuits.'

Alice spent almost half an hour talking to him, drinking black coffee liberally sprinkled with sawdust – it didn't appear to affect the flavour – and nibbling biscuits which, while good, weren't a patch on Ines's home-made ones. He told her he would be delighted to buy an almost unlimited amount of timber from the Varaldo family. When he started asking technical questions about the species, age, height and other dimensions of the trees on the estate, she told him honestly that she had limited experience of forestry, and he offered to give his advice. In the first instance he said he would be happy to come up to the estate and inspect the woods and give his opinion as to which trees would be more saleable. He then went on make a fascinating proposal. If the family agreed, he would be prepared to do a deal in which he would provide all the manpower and machinery needed for felling the chosen trees, and his people would also transport the timber from the estate to the sawmill. It would then be up to Alfonso and Pietro to replant with young saplings so as to maintain the sustainable development of the woodland.

The more Alice listened to him, the more the idea took shape in her head. His proposal had considerable appeal: first of all, he and his people obviously had the expertise and the expensive machinery that she and the family lacked, and just as importantly, doing a deal with him would avoid almost any capital outlay for the family at a time when they were going to have to count their pennies very carefully. She arranged with Rocco that he would meet her on site next morning at ten and she resolved to make sure that Alfonso would also be there to meet him. She advised Rocco that the decision would then have to be taken by the baron and his family, but that if she felt it was a good deal, she would do her best to recommend it to them.

By the time she left, she and Rocco were on first name terms and he had shown her photos of his twin daughters in their First Communion dresses. She got the feeling that underneath the tough guy exterior, Rocco was really a pussycat.

Her visit to the church in the little village of Santa Margherita produced mixed results. When she got there she discovered that although the scaffolding was still standing, there was nobody at work. There was a large white sign attached to the scaffolding with the name of the builders, permit numbers, and details of the architects responsible for the work. This was one of the firms she recognised from her search on the Internet. She made a note of it and tried the church door in the hope of being able to speak to the priest himself and see if he would be prepared to give an unbiased opinion of the architect and, indeed, the builders. Alas, the door was locked and there was no sign of anybody to ask. In fact there was no sign of life anywhere except for a café on the opposite side of the piazza which looked open, so Alice went over to see if anybody could provide any information.

There were only four people inside the café: three elderly gentlemen playing cards in one corner and an equally elderly man behind the bar. He greeted Alice and asked if she would like anything. She was still picking pieces of sawdust out of her teeth after her coffee at the sawmill, but nothing else immediately came to mind, so she asked for an espresso. She stood at the bar to drink it and gradually got into a conversation with the barman. It rapidly emerged that this barista appeared to know all there was to know about the village of Santa Margherita including the work on the church – or the lack of it.

'The scaffolding's been up for almost six months now, but nothing much seems to get done. I've spoken to the men who turn up from time to time to work on the roof, but they sound pretty clueless if you ask me.'

'Isn't there an architect's firm supervising the work?'

'If there is, I haven't seen them. I don't know what the problem is. Some people say it's because the bishop hasn't given Father Ignazio the money to pay for the repairs, but others say it's because the builders are incompetent or because the architect drew the plans all wrong. Whatever the reason, nothing's been done for ages.'

Alice finished her drink and thanked the man for the information, mentally removing that particular architect from her list of possibles.

As she drove out of the village she noticed a fine old stone house set in a large garden, just off the road. What caught her eye wasn't the garden, however, but scaffolding at the side of the house. She spotted a figure in the garden so, on impulse, she pulled in and stopped. A mature lady came over to the hedge and greeted her.

'Hello, are you lost?'

'No, I'm fine, thanks. It's just that I'm looking for a good architect and I couldn't help noticing that you've got some building work going on. I don't suppose you can recommend a firm familiar with old, historical properties, like your lovely house?'

The woman smiled at her. 'We certainly can. My husband's an architect and he knows everything about all the architects in the area. He's inside now if you'd like to talk to him.

'That's very kind, but I wouldn't want to disturb you or him.'

'Not at all. I've just been doing a bit of gardening and he's reading his book. Do come in and I'll make some coffee. My name's Margherita, like the village.'

Alice introduced herself and followed Margherita to the house where she stopped to admire the sculpted stone-work around the entrance. 'I could see from the road that your house was old, but I hadn't realised your house was so *very* old. This looks like Renaissance or even medieval stonework.'

'Fourteen ninety-two, the year Columbus set off looking for the spice islands and ended up in the Caribbean.' The voice came from a tall, white-haired gentleman who emerged on the doorstep. 'The date's sculpted on the inside of the lintel. It's good to meet somebody who knows their architecture.' He extended his hand towards her. 'Virgilio Bolognese at your service.' His language was very formal but there was a twinkle in his eye.

His wife followed Alice inside. 'Virgilio, this young lady's asking about architects and I told her I was married to one. Why don't you take her into the lounge while I make some coffee?'

Alice was soon seated opposite Signor Bolognese in a charming room with a vaulted ceiling. After introducing herself to him, she explained who she was and what she was doing, and he immediately looked most interested.

'Well, well, well, so Varaldo castle's going to be open to the public. Do let me know when that happens and I'll definitely come along for a look. I don't know anybody who's been in there, but I'm sure it must have some wonderful features. I'm retired now, have been for seven years, and I have quite a bit of experience of medieval and Renaissance buildings, but I've never had the chance to visit Varaldo. It sounds like an enviable job you have. My congratulations.'

'What a pity you're retired. You would have been exactly what I'm looking for. You see, I'm on the hunt for an architect with experience of historic buildings like the castle. Maybe you could give me a few names.'

'Of course, of course, I'd be delighted to. Ah, here's Margherita with the coffee. Margherita, did you realise that this young lady's English? She speaks such good Italian I wouldn't have known.' He lowered his voice. 'There are a couple of English families who have holiday homes in the village, but they speak less Italian than I do English.' He grinned 'And all I can say is "Good Morning".' He delivered the last two words in a fine attempt at an English accent. 'The trouble comes when I run into them in the afternoon or evening – I never learnt the appropriate greetings for later in the day. Anyway, do tell us, please, how it is that a charming English lady is responsible for one of Italy's finest old buildings – and how it is you speak better Italian than I do.'

Alice gave them a brief summary of how she had ended up here. She mentioned her time in the Dolomites and at the Manor, and Signor Bolognese looked impressed. She was mildly impressed herself that she found it possible to talk about her years in the mountains without qualms. This had to be progress. The architect chatted to her at some length about historic buildings in Britain that he would have liked to visit, and Alice told him about the estate management course she had done. Finally, as she took her last sip of the rapidly cooling coffee, idly reflecting that with so much caffeine in her system she was probably going to find it hard to get to sleep tonight, she brought him around to the subject of architects, and he demonstrated that his claim to know all about local firms was no mere boast.

While she scribbled in her notebook, he ran through almost a dozen different architects' studios in Parma, detailing their advantages and disadvantages until she had a pretty clear idea of those best qualified and experienced for what she wanted. Unsurprisingly the architects responsible for Santa Margherita church received a scathing review. After a bit of discussion, they agreed on a shortlist of three: two old established firms and one relatively new one. Interestingly, when she pressed him for his number one choice, he came down on the side of the new company.

'Together with my studio work, I also taught for many years at Parma university, and one of my best students is the man behind this relatively new studio. They've only been in existence for four or five years, but they've already gained an excellent reputation. Luca, his name is. After qualifying, he went off to work down south of Rome for a number of years and he told me he was involved in the restoration of several castles as well as an abandoned medieval village. He certainly has the experience and I'm sure you'd get on well with him. Yes, when you make an appointment, ask for Luca – and mention my name.'

Alice thanked the two of the most warmly for their hospitality and for the valuable advice, and she promised Signor Bolognese that she would invite him for a private visit to the castle before any of the major work started. He gave her his card, kissed her hand, and she left with the conviction she had just made two new friends.

Chapter 13

Alice spent the week exploring the castle and its grounds, making appointments to see architects and tradesmen, and setting about clearing a workspace for herself. Although Simonetta offered her a choice of fine rooms on the first floor for her use, Alice was determined to establish her own domain as soon as possible so as not to intrude upon the family. She installed herself in the room she'd already earmarked as her office during her first thorough inspection of the castle. It was still filled with all manner of junk and inhabited by some truly scary arachnids as well as rodents and she was more than happy to accept an offer of help from Alfonso and Pietro.

It was clear that some of the junk lying submerged under a network of cobwebs, so dense it almost looked like a sheet, had been there for decades if not centuries. Among the mouldy clothes, worm-eaten furniture and broken pots and bottles they came across a number of real gems. Alfonso and his son found no fewer than five vicious spearheads, their wooden shafts now so rotten they crumbled away as the men picked them up. Along with them were three or four rusty bowl-shaped helmets and even a fine longsword, so heavy that Alice had trouble lifting it even using both her hands. The leather of its handle had rotted in parts but it was still a magnificent artefact and when Alice showed the finds to the baron, his eyes lit up and he told her he would make sure that the sword and the other pieces of military memorabilia were carefully stored in readiness for display in the new castle museum when it opened.

There was no form of heating but hopefully for the next four or five months she wouldn't need any, and by the time autumn arrived there should be a new central heating system in operation. As far as furniture was concerned, once she had spent a whole morning scrubbing the floors and walls as clean as she could, she picked out a desk and a couple of chairs from under one of the dustsheets on the first floor which, while nice, weren't special enough to put on display. Her two willing helpers carted the furniture downstairs and set it up, and Alfonso even managed to find a working desk light that he proudly set in place.

'There, signora, it looks like an office already.'

'Thank you both so much for all your help and, remember, it's Alice, not signora. Okay?'

Alfonso and his son had both been with her on Tuesday morning when Rocco from the sawmill had come to inspect the surrounding woods. Rocco had been most impressed with the variety, age and condition of the trees and he went off promising to send her a plan of action and a written offer of collaboration which would hopefully benefit both sides. As for Alfonso and Pietro, they appeared delighted to see that things were starting to happen at long last and Alice got the feeling that Ines might be changing her mind about their willingness to work.

In particular, the men were enthusiastic, if slightly mystified, by the idea of breeding alpacas and, once her office was set up, they went off to select the most suitable fields for livestock and to start mending and replacing rotten fences and strengthening walls. Unlike Devon, this area had no hedges and Alice noticed that most of the local farmers used electric fences to create fields in the wide, open grasslands, so they did the same. Alfonso, who knew most of the farmers in the area, promised to put out feelers as to where they could get hold of alpacas. After consultation with Simonetta, Alice asked him to investigate the cost of replacing the old tractor – which she felt sure should end up in the castle museum – and buying a quadbike, one of the necessities on a modern farm that her father swore by. The response from Alfonso and his son had been barely concealed delight.

As for cattle, Alice decided to wait until the castle was open and producing decent regular income before embarking on the considerable expense of setting up a proper modern milking parlour. The beauty of the alpacas was that they were hardy animals and her father had assured her that they didn't need very much in terms of initial outlay apart from just buying the animals and then shearing them once a year. She had been reading articles online and had ordered a book in Italian written by an alpaca farmer up north near Turin. Her father also promised to send her a copy of the book he had been reading so that she could build up as much knowledge as possible about this rather unusual animal. By the end of the week, she was definitely getting the feeling that the plans were starting to come together.

She knew the most important first step was to decide on an architect and she made three appointments in Parma for Friday afternoon with the firms recommended by

Signor Bolognese. She drove down early and spent the morning going around the city, trying to sort out the bureaucratic headaches involved with resuming employment here in Italy after a four-year gap. Fortunately, she still had a sheaf of documents left over from when she had worked over here before and, even better, she had kept her Italian bank account and tax code. Even so, she was feeling shell-shocked by the time she emerged from the last of the offices and headed for a café under one of the *portici*, the covered arcades that lined the busy shopping streets, where she sat down gratefully to relax with a sandwich and a long glass of cold mineral water.

She had arranged things so as to start the afternoon's interviews with the two older firms that Signor Bolognese had recommended, before finishing off with his first choice, the newest of the three, LM Architects. That way she would be able to compare each of them and choose one to present to the family for their approval next week during what was becoming a regular Monday morning meeting.

All three firms were within walking distance of each other in the centre of Parma. Unlike the previous time when she had spent the night here after her interview, she had managed to get into the city and find a parking space without getting totally confused by the lack of road signs and the one-way system. She left the car and went to her first appointment where she was seen by an elderly gentleman with white hair, not dissimilar to Signor Bolognese in appearance, although his manner was less affable. He was courteous and polite, but it seemed to Alice that he was a bit too self-important and she had a feeling that, however wide and varied his experience might be, she was likely to find herself constantly fighting to get her own way. She wanted an architect she could work with, not for.

The second architects' studio was less than a hundred metres along the same street. This time she was seen by a woman. Probably in her late fifties, she was elegantly dressed, absolutely dripping with gold and with long blood-red fingernails. Although she, too, was polite, there was no warmth there, and from the schedule of charges that she gave Alice it was clear that employing her firm would cost an arm and a leg. After all, designer clothes and manicures didn't come cheap. Alice was, therefore, far from optimistic when she arrived at her third and final appointment of the day.

Unlike the previous two offices, the last studio was situated in a relatively modern building, just on the edge of the *centro storico*. Alice took the lift to the top floor and stepped out into a light and airy lobby with a panoramic window looking out over the roofs of the city. The sign on the glass door in front of her indicated that she had arrived at LM Architects. She opened it and walked in to be greeted by a young man in his early twenties sitting behind a glass-topped desk. He looked up and produced a friendly smile as Alice walked in.

'Signora Sterling? You've come to see Luca?'

Alice smiled back. 'That's right. I'm told he's the man to see about historic building works.'

'He certainly is.' The receptionist pressed a button and spoke into an intercom on his desk. 'Signora Sterling's here, Luca. Shall I show her in?'

'Yes, please, Carlo.' The voice sounded as if it belonged to another young man, and when Carlo opened a door and ushered her in, Alice saw that the architect was probably only three or four years older than she was, but it wasn't his age that struck her most forcibly. As the receptionist retreated, closing the door behind him, Alice momentarily lost the power of speech, her eyes trained on the fair-haired man sitting behind another glass-topped desk, a familiar spark of attraction shooting through her. She might well have stayed there, rooted to the spot, if there hadn't been a movement from beneath the desk. A big black dog roused himself from his master's feet and came padding across the tiled floor towards her, his tail wagging lazily. As he did so, the architect stood up with a look of amazement on his face.

'It's you... from the restaurant.' He sounded as surprised as she felt.

She did her best to kick herself into gear and attempted a reply, keeping her eyes trained on the big black dog at her feet who was nuzzling her with his nose. 'I was just going to say the exact same thing. I didn't know you were an architect.' Simonetta hadn't said anything about this.

'And I didn't know I was going to see you again so soon.' He followed his dog across to her and they shook hands. Alice felt an almost electric thrill run through her as they did so, and she hastily dropped her eyes to the dog again as she felt her cheeks flush.

After counting to ten and taking a deep breath she steeled herself to look up from the dog again and saw a hint of a smile on his face, no doubt caused by the bewildered expression on her face. 'But your name's Luca...'

'That's right. Luca Montorso, and Carlo told me you're Alice Sterling.' He indicated a seat in front of his desk. As her befuddled brain gradually began to register what she had just heard, she sank down gratefully onto the stylish steel and leather chair and took a couple of deep breaths.

'I thought your name was Tommaso...'

Comprehension dawned on his face. 'I see what's happened. You're confusing me with my twin brother. His name's Tommaso. I'm Luca.'

Alice realised she must be coming across as a complete idiot so she dropped her eyes to the dog again, who had come over and was now resting his nose on her lap. She sat there stroking his ears while trying to make sense of what she had just learned. Twin brothers! So presumably Luca was the one who had run off and left home after a fight with his father while Tommaso had stayed at the farm. As she slowly started to process the possible ramifications of this discovery, his voice intruded on her thoughts.

'It's very good to see you again. Can I get you something to drink?' From his tactful tone she got the feeling he was deliberately giving her a bit of time to sort her head out.

Finally raising her eyes from the dog once more, she did her best to sound a bit less gormless. 'If you're going to have something, I'd love an espresso.' Although the way she was feeling, something stronger might have been more welcome.

'Of course. It'll give me a chance to show off my new coffee machine. I hope you like it.'

He went across to the corner of the room and busied himself with the coffee machine, while Alice came to terms with the fact that she was now in the same space as the man who had so unexpectedly produced that spark of attraction in her in the restaurant.

And he wasn't Simonetta's boyfriend after all.

As the realisation dawned on her that this meant that he wasn't off limits after all, bewilderment was replaced by something more akin to apprehension, and the unfamiliar self-confidence she had felt the other night in the restaurant threatened to evaporate completely. He was most probably already in a relationship, but what if he wasn't? What would happen if he asked her out? What would she say? Would it be a good idea to consider dating a member of the Montorso tribe? Would he be interested in her?

Her brain was still spinning when he came back over with two little cups of coffee.

'Do you want sugar?'

The simple banality of the question finally shook her out of her contemplative state and she gave herself a mental kicking. She was in her thirties, not a teenager. It was about time she got a grip. She took the cup and smiled up at him.

'No, no sugar thanks. This is very kind of you. Sorry for my moment of confusion.'

'Don't worry about it. It's happened to me all my life. That's the problem with having an identical twin.' He walked back around his desk and sat down again. 'It can have its advantages. At school, from time to time, I'd take my brother's maths tests for him, and he'd occasionally take my place in the football team after I hurt my back. Nobody ever realised.' He sipped his coffee. 'Be careful, the coffee's very hot. Now, how can I help you? I believe you told Carlo you have an old property that needs restoration.'

'It's not quite as simple as that. The property doesn't belong to me, I've been employed to manage it.' She took a deep breath and kept her eyes on his face as she broke the news to him. 'It's Varaldo castle.' She saw his eyes widen. 'That's right, I've been employed by the Varaldo family. They intend to open the castle to the public. It's going to need a lot of renovation and modernisation, and then of course there'll be all sorts of bureaucratic hoops to jump through. That's why we need a good architect, and you come very highly recommended.'

'I do?'

She went on to tell him about her chance encounter with Signor Bolognese and this drew a smile from him, but she could see that he was hesitant. She could well imagine what must be going through his mind at being asked to work for the family who had been sworn enemies of his own family for centuries. Generations of his fore-fathers were probably turning in their graves just at the thought of it. There was no point in beating about the bush so she decided to tackle the subject head on.

'As you can probably imagine, since coming here, I've learnt that relations between the two families are strained and have been for a long, long time. Before coming here today, I had no idea who you were, and if I had known, I probably wouldn't have come. The last thing I want would be to put you in a difficult position or to stir up further ill feelings. Now that I know who you are, if you'd prefer not to get involved, I'll understand perfectly, although I'm sure it's going to be a really interesting project. If you tell me you prefer to stay out of it, I'll finish my coffee and leave. I wouldn't want to waste your time, but it would be great if you were prepared to consider it.'

She found herself questioning her true motives in trying to persuade this man to accept a commission which would throw him into direct conflict with his own family, even assuming that the baron would be prepared to accept help from a Montorso. She tried telling herself that it was simply because he had been personally recommended by Signor Bolognese, but she knew that wasn't the real reason. In a moment of self-awareness, she realised that she liked this man and the idea of spending more time with him had a lot of appeal. Whether he would want to spend time with her remained to be seen and she wasn't holding her breath. Either way, this was hardly the most professional of motives for choosing somebody to head up a project on this scale.

Seeing him looking uncertain, she went on to outline the sorts of changes she had in mind and the serious amount of input she would require from him. The more she spoke, the more interest she could see on his face. She could well imagine how appealing a major heritage project like this could be to a young architect with a relatively new business. It occurred to her that the name of the studio, LM Architects, was made up of his initials, so presumably he was the main or maybe even the only partner. Apart from anything else, a project like this could also prove to be very lucrative to him, so she had a fair idea of the sort of inner conflict he might be experiencing. When she had finished detailing how she saw the job developing, she sat back and reached for her coffee.

He didn't reply immediately and the dog, who had been sitting happily by her side, got up and trotted across to his master to lend a bit of canine support, maybe sensing that he was struggling with a difficult decision. Finally, Luca Montorso looked up from the Labrador and nodded a couple of times.

'First of all, thank you for coming to me about this. It certainly sounds like a fascinating project and I must admit it's something that has considerable appeal, but I'm sure you can understand my hesitation. It's not just a simple business decision because of the situation between the two families with which you're already familiar.'

He hesitated and then corrected himself.

'I'm sorry, I'm making it sound as if you've offered me the job already and I wouldn't want to sound presumptuous. Why don't I tell you a bit about my background and experience and give you my thoughts on how I feel you should proceed? If you're interested in asking me to work with you, then I would just ask for a little bit of time to think things through and talk them over with my brother, before giving you my definite response. You don't mind, do you? I wouldn't want you to think I'm trying to sound ungrateful. Like I say, it was very good of you to come to me about this.'

Alice nodded. 'Of course I understand, and I'd better put my cards on the table as well. Any recommendation I make will have to be ratified by the family, and it could be I'll have a hard job to convince the baron that you're the right person.' She gave him a little smile. 'Life can be very complicated at times.'

She spent almost an hour with him, going through in greater detail what she had in mind and showing him some of the photos she had taken to illustrate the current state of the building. In return, he told her about the six years he had spent working in Latina and Abruzzo, south of Rome, including iconic places like Montecassino. He also talked her through two recent heritage projects he had undertaken here in Emilia-Romagna and, in particular, he appeared to be well versed in the crippling amount of paperwork to be submitted to the relevant authorities when dealing with historic properties. He invited her to contact his previous clients in order to get references as to his ability. It certainly sounded as if he had a lot of experience and the more they talked, the more convinced she became that, irrespective of any nascent feelings she might be developing for this man she barely knew, from a work perspective LM Architects looked like they were the right people for the job.

Last of all they talked money and she was pleased to find that his rates, while certainly not cheap, compared favourably with the previous two firms she had interviewed. Without the complication of the family feud, she would have had no hesitation in offering him the job. As it was, she told him she would speak to Simonetta and promised to give him an answer the following day. As that would be Saturday, he gave her his mobile number so she could text him. If the answer was yes, at that point he told her he would sit down and talk to his brother and he promised her a reply by first thing on Monday morning.

He stood up and thanked her once more and they shook hands. Once again, his touch sent a little shockwave through her but she was better prepared this time and she managed to avoid blushing like a teenager. Before leaving she asked him something which had been puzzling her.

'Do you still live in Varaldo? I assume you must be somewhere near there as I've seen you in the restaurant twice.'

He shook his head. 'No, I live here in Parma now. If I were to return to live in Varaldo, I'd be bound to run into my father sooner or later and I never want to see him again. I don't know if you've heard on the grapevine, but he and I had a major falling-out years ago and I left home for good. I haven't seen him or spoken to him since my university days. The only reason I go back to Varaldo is because one of my best friends is Leo Chiesa, who's taken over from his father as chef at the Casa Rosa. His father and my father don't get on – to be honest, a lot of people don't get on with my father – and the two of them haven't spoken for years, so I know I'm quite safe in the restaurant. There's no way my father would ever set foot in there and more fool him. If you haven't already tried it, Leo and his father make the best lasagne in the world.'

He accompanied her to the door and opened it for her. She stopped and turned towards him one last time, feeling remarkably awkward. 'Thank you for your time, Signor Montorso. I promise I'll be in touch tomorrow.'

'Thank you for coming.' He sounded equally awkward and for a moment or two she intercepted a curious glance from his receptionist who must have picked up on his tone. 'Call me Luca, please.'

Chapter 14

Next morning Alice had arranged to meet Simonetta at the stables and she was keen to tell her all about her meeting with the three architects, particularly with Luca and his canine companion. To her surprise and considerable relief, when she mentioned his name, this actually produced a smile on Simonetta's face.

'When you were asking about architects, I didn't want to mention Luca in front of Papà and Nonna and I wondered if you might contact him. Tommaso's often told me his brother's a very good architect. I've heard that from other people as well and I'm sure he'd be great for us. I was going to tell you about him on a couple of occasions during the week but each time the thought of the family complications it might cause stopped me. In the end I told myself that if you were to choose him, it had to be some sort of sign and we would just have to do our best to make it work.'

Simonetta waited until the horses had negotiated a narrow gateway and were once again walking side by side before she continued.

'So, what do you think? Is Luca the best of the architects you've seen? We both know it's going to be difficult if he is.'

Alice answered honestly. 'I have absolutely no doubt that he *is* the best candidate, but I'm sure you're right that it could provoke all sorts of problems. Most important of all, do you think your father could accept having a Montorso working for him?'

Simonetta took her time before replying. 'I think he'll take a lot of persuading but, ultimately, the deciding factor will be my grandmother. If we can get her on our side then I'm sure Papà will say yes, probably reluctantly, but I think he would agree. Are you doing anything tomorrow afternoon? Maybe you and I should sit down together with Nonna and have a quiet chat in advance of Monday's meeting.'

'That's fine by me. Good idea. What about Luca and Tommaso's father? How do you think he's likely to react? Don't let's forget that, as mayor, he's probably able to create a lot of bureaucratic complications. And what about his relationship with Luca? If it's bad now, presumably seeing him working for you would only make it worse.'

'From what Tommi's told me, there's absolutely no love lost between Luca and his father as it is. They haven't seen or spoken to each other for years, so it can hardly make their relationship any worse. And, to be honest, the same could be said about relations between our two families. Cesare Montorso has always hated us and I can't see that changing. There's no way he was ever going to make things easy for us with this project so, again, I don't think we'll necessarily be any worse off if we go with Luca.'

'Okay, if you're sure, I'll send him a text and tell him I'm going to put his name forward at our meeting on Monday.'

'Do that, but I still think it'll be a good idea if you and I sit down with Nonna before the meeting to see if we can convince her to be on our side. Leave Achille to me; I know how to handle him.'

They crossed back to the castle side of the valley and were soon riding on Varaldo family land. Alice followed the directions given to her by Alfonso so that she could show Simonetta the fields where the alpacas were to be kept. From there they rode on into the woods and she pointed out the trees which Rocco felt should be harvested first. Simonetta took photos to show her father and told Alice that now that he had accepted the inevitable, he was beginning to sound a bit more enthusiastic. Apparently he had even been seen reading a book on animal husbandry taken from the extensive castle library, but because many of the volumes were over a century old, he had been unable to find anything definitive dealing with alpacas over here in Europe. Alice promised to lend him the new book she had ordered once she had had a chance to look at it.

It was just starting to rain when they returned to the stables and Alice went home to dry out and do her laundry which she had been putting off all week. Before making a start, she sent a text to Luca Montorso telling him she had spoken to Simonetta and that they were both convinced he was the right man for the job. She reminded him that this would be subject to approval at the Varaldo family meeting on Monday morning and asked if he could let her know his answer one way or the other before then. As she pressed Send she couldn't help hoping that he would agree, and that the family would endorse her recommendation. This, she told herself, was purely based on his suitability as an architect, but she knew, deep down, that there was more to it than that.

She had just put her delicates into the sink to soak when she heard her phone bleep. It was a reply from Luca.

> Thank you both very much for the vote of confidence. I promise I'll get back to you by tomorrow night. Thanks again.

A few minutes later she received another text, this time from Simonetta.

> Tea with Nonna all fixed up for tomorrow afternoon. She normally has a rest after lunch, so would four o'clock be okay?

—

The following day Alice walked up to the castle at four o'clock and was met by Simonetta at the front door with a conspiratorial grin on her face. 'Achille's gone out for the afternoon and Papà's down in the cellars poking about, looking for historic bits and pieces for his museum. That was a brilliant idea of yours; he's really excited at the thought of creating a lasting exhibition of family history. This means we should have Nonna to ourselves.'

Tea with Simonetta's grandmother was taken in the baroness's own private drawing room. Alice had never been in here before and she cast an appreciative eye around as she followed Simonetta over to a beautiful old brocade-covered couch. Though smaller than the family lounge where they had their meetings, this was still a large room, and it needed to be, because a third of it was taken up by a massive grand piano. The baroness was sitting in an armchair by the empty fireplace and she waved the two of them towards her.

'Come and sit down, girls. Would you like tea or coffee? Alice, maybe you'd prefer tea.'

Alice sat down alongside Simonetta on the couch. 'I'm happy with either, thank you. I'll have what you're having.'

They chatted idly for a few minutes until Silvia had brought in a teapot, cups and saucers, and even a jug of cold milk which Alice had not been expecting, seeing as here in Italy tea was normally drunk black, maybe with a slice of lemon. Along with the tea was a magnificent-looking chocolate cake. After seeing that everybody had been served, Silvia left the room, and the baroness looked across at her granddaughter with a suspicious smile on her face.

'It's very nice to see both of you but I know you well, Simonetta. There's something on your mind, isn't there?'

Alice couldn't help smiling. Although she might be getting on in years, there really was nothing wrong with this lady's antennae. Alice sipped her tea while Simonetta explained the problem that now faced them, finishing with the words, 'So you see, Nonna, we both feel that he's the best architect for the job, but we're afraid that Papà won't approve. What do you think?'

The baroness had been listening closely without comment to everything her granddaughter had said, and the three of them sat in silence for almost a minute before the old lady spoke. 'Do you trust this man?'

Simonetta and Alice nodded in tandem and Simonetta replied straightaway. 'Yes, I do.'

'But surely, you haven't spoken to him. Didn't you say only Alice went to see him? Have *you* ever met him?' She really didn't miss a trick.

Alice now knew from what Simonetta had told her during their ride the previous day that she and Tommaso had met up with his brother in Parma on many occasions in the past, but, of course, revealing that to her grandmother would mean revealing her hidden love affair, and that would risk opening a whole fresh can of worms. Thinking quickly, Alice leapt in to help out.

'I certainly got the feeling that he was trustworthy. There was just something about him.' She searched desperately for something else to say in his support, but the baroness was not going to be put off the scent so easily.

'I'm very pleased to hear that, Alice, but I was asking Simonetta.' She didn't say it nastily, but she made it clear that she wanted to hear from her granddaughter. That was a brief pause before Simonetta replied.

'Achille and I sometimes met him. We met both brothers, when we were younger. You know, at local fairs and football matches and things like that.'

'Of course, but people can change as they grow older. Maybe he's no longer a simple, innocent little boy.'

'Yes, but...'

Seeing that Simonetta was floundering, Alice tried another intervention. 'I heard that he had a major falling-out with his father a long time ago and apparently the two of them haven't spoken for years and years. Surely that's in his favour.'

'Who told you that?'

Alice felt the baroness's shrewd old eyes studying her. It had been Alfonso the groundsman who had first given her this piece of information but she felt she had better leave him out of it just in case he got into trouble as a result for talking out of turn.

'Luca Montorso himself, when I visited his studio on Friday.' The baroness nodded before redirecting her attention to her granddaughter.

'But he didn't tell *you*, did he, Simonetta. Is there something you haven't told me?'

After another long silence, Simonetta finally gave in. 'Yes, there is, Nonna, and I'm afraid you aren't going to like it.'

'Why don't you let me be the judge of that? The older I get, the less things seem to bother me.'

Alice shot a sideways glance at Simonetta and could see the worry on her face as she set about explaining the length and depth of her relationship with Tommaso, finishing with the words, 'It all started years ago, but we've only really been together properly for the last three or four years.'

'You and Luca Montorso?'

'Not Luca. His brother, Tommaso; they're twins.'

Alice did her best to make it look as if she was staring out of the window at the hills on the opposite side of the valley while at the same time keeping a surreptitious eye on the baroness's face. She hadn't been quite sure what to expect – outrage maybe – but the old lady's features hardly changed at all.

'So you're telling me that you're in love with a member of the Montorso family?'

'Yes, I am.' Simonetta was trying to sound resolute but Alice could hear the insecurity in her voice.

'And you've felt this way for a number of years, but you haven't dared say anything to your father or me about it?'

'Yes, Nonna.'

Alice didn't want to swivel her head around so as to look at Simonetta, but from the way her voice cracked, it sounded as though she was about to burst into tears. It must have seemed that way to her grandmother as well, because she was quick to reply.

'I never cease to amaze at how silly people can be. What's wrong with falling in love? Some people go through their whole lives without knowing love, so you can consider yourself a very lucky girl.'

'Yes, but he's a Montorso...'

'My dear girl, in this day and age it wouldn't matter in the slightest if he was a little green man or a two-headed woman. We've moved on since medieval times.'

'You don't mind?' Simonetta's voice was little more than a croak.

'Of course I don't. Times have changed. I just wish your father could get that into his head and, indeed, the same applies to the father of your beloved Tommaso. Now come over here and let me give you a hug. It takes me too long to get up.'

Simonetta jumped to her feet and almost flung herself into her grandmother's arms. From the way her shoulders were shaking, it was pretty clear to Alice that she was crying now and she felt her own eyes stinging with emotion in sympathy. The two of them stayed like that for almost a minute before Simonetta pulled herself out of her grandmother's arms and perched on the arm of the chair beside her, wiping her eyes with a tissue.

'And you really don't mind? You're sure?'

'Of course I'm sure. In fact, I'm delighted for you. I've been thinking for some years now that it was about time you found yourself a husband. So, are you planning on marrying him?'

Simonetta nodded vigorously. 'We'd love to get married, but it's so terribly complicated.'

'Well, listen to me, it doesn't need to be complicated as far as our family are concerned. *Amor vincit omnia*, remember that. Love conquers all. You're free to marry whoever you like, and I look forward to meeting Tommaso... and his brother.'

'Does that mean you don't mind if we employ Luca to be our architect?'

'If he's the best person for the job, then you need to employ him. As far as I'm concerned, if you and Alice think he's the one, then you'll have my full support.'

'But what about Papà? How do you think he's going to react if we tell him we want to employ Luca, and what if I then tell him that I'm in love with Tommaso? He'll have a fit.'

'Your father inherited his belief in the sanctity of the family from his father, and he inherited that from countless generations before him, but just as your father's seen the wisdom of trying to generate a profit from our home and its lands, I'm sure we can convince him of the suitability of the two brothers.'

'You said "we." Does that mean you'll help persuade him?'

'Of course I will. Now, ring the bell for Ines or Silvia, would you?'

A few seconds later Ines herself arrived and the baroness called her over. 'Ines, I've just had some very good news, and we need to celebrate. Could you find a cold bottle of French champagne and three glasses please?' She stopped and corrected herself. 'On second thoughts, make that five glasses and ask Silvia to come back with you.'

Minutes later all five of them had glasses of champagne in their hands, including the embarrassed-looking house-keeper and her daughter. Waving away Simonetta's offer of help, the baroness got to her feet and held out her glass towards them all.

'I've just heard from my granddaughter that she's found a man she wants to marry. I couldn't be happier, and if this doesn't deserve a toast, I don't know what does.'

They all clinked glasses together and tried the cham-pagne. It tasted excellent, and quite rightly so. From where she was standing, Alice could see that this was no ordinary champagne. The date on the bottle indicated that it was fifteen years old and she wondered how much a wine like this might be worth. For a second or two she reverted to her role as castle manager, curious if there might be a cellar beneath their feet packed with racks of precious wines worth a small fortune. She would need to look.

Simonetta was hanging on to her grandmother's free arm with one hand and was visibly overwhelmed. Ines and Silvia were looking uncomfortable to be here drinking champagne with the baroness, but were no doubt pleased to be included. From the expression on Silvia's face it was clear that she was dying to know the identity of the man of Simonetta's dreams but this was not revealed for now. Obviously the baron had to be informed first. Alice rather hoped that she herself wouldn't be there when that happened. She had had quite enough drama for one afternoon.

That evening she once again went to the Casa Rosa for dinner. Tonight, however, there was no sign of Luca, but partway through the best lasagne she had ever tasted, she got a text from him.

> Alea iacta est. I believe that's what Julius Caesar said when he crossed the Rubicon. I've spoken to my brother and we both feel that this is something I should do, whatever the consequences. Thank you for the commission. On behalf of LM Architects I'm delighted to accept. If the Varaldo family agree, please let me know when it would be convenient for me to make an initial visit to the property. Thanks again. Luca Montorso.

All very formal, but it was the reply Alice had been hoping for. Now the next bridge to be crossed was that of getting Simonetta's father to agree, and in spite of having enlisted the support of the baroness, she knew that wasn't going to be easy.

Chapter 15

Next morning Alice was at the castle early to meet up with Simonetta in preparation for the family meeting. After going through all the items on the agenda, she gently enquired whether Simonetta had broken the news to her father of her relationship with Tommaso. Simonetta gave a little smile and shook her head.

'I've been waiting for the right moment and it never seems to come.' She caught Alice's eye. 'Yes, I know, I should just get on with it. I know I have to sit down and have it out with him sooner rather than later, but I'm nervous as to what he'll say.'

Alice gave her a reassuring smile. 'It'll be fine. Remember what your grandmother said yesterday: times have changed and love conquers all.'

Simonetta gave a weak smile in response. 'I'm afraid love has got a lot of conquering to do if it's going to bring about peace between our two families. Even if Papà's okay with it, I'm terrified of how Tommaso's father is going to react when he hears the news.'

'Maybe when he sees that your family have accepted the situation, he'll do the right thing.'

'And maybe he won't. Anyway, first things first, we need to get my father onside as far as Luca's concerned. Even with Nonna's help, that's going to be tough. Don't forget that he has row upon row of ancestors behind him telling him he should be doing the opposite.'

'It'll be all right, I'm sure. I have the utmost faith in your grandmother. She's quite a lady.'

When the meeting started, Alice toyed with the idea of working through all the other less contentious items on the agenda first, before bringing up the subject of Luca, but as this was without question the most important decision to be taken, she decided to tackle it head on.

Taking a deep breath, she addressed herself directly to the baron. 'I spent Friday interviewing a number of architects in Parma and one studio in particular impressed me. It's a relatively new company called LM Architects. They have a lot of experience and their rates compare favourably with the others I saw.' She waited until he started nodding in approval before dropping the bombshell. 'The architect in charge who would be dealing with our project is called Luca Montorso.' It took a second or two to register but when it did, the baron's face darkened.

'Did you say Montorso? Is that one of the Montorso family from here?' He looked around belligerently. 'Of course it is, they only exist in this area.'

As he paused to draw breath, Alice confirmed Luca's identity. 'He's the son of the mayor of Varaldo, but he and his father had a major row many years ago and they haven't seen or spoken to each other since.'

'Even so, do you mean to say that you're suggesting we give oversight of our whole project to one of our sworn enemies with whom we've been fighting for centuries?' He snorted. 'It's unthinkable!'

Alice was about to attempt a defence of her selection when the baroness stepped in. 'Listen to yourself,

Lodovico, just listen to yourself. Can't you hear how ridiculous you sound? This is the twenty-first century now, not the Middle Ages. Time has moved on and so must we. The girls are convinced that this man is the right one for the job and I think we should stand behind them and accept their decision.'

'But a Montorso…?' The indignation had gone out of the baron's voice, to be replaced by an almost child-like pleading tone. 'We can't, Mamma, we really can't. What would Papà have said? It's unthinkable after all these years…'

'Tell me what good this senseless feud ever did for either family. Ever since I married your father, I tried to get him to modify his attitude. Yes, there's been bad blood for centuries and unpleasant things happened during the last war, but we have to move on. If it helps you make up your mind, I can tell you that your father used those exact same words to me twenty years ago. He told me it was time to move on. In fact, if it hadn't been for his heart failure, I feel convinced he would have done his best to bury the hatchet.'

The baron was looking astounded. 'He really said that to you? After everything that happened during the war?'

'Forgive and forget, and if you can't forget, Lodovico, at least forgive.'

The baron subsided into resigned silence and, after waiting for a minute or so, Alice went on with the meeting, working through the various agenda points relating to fields to be used, rooms to be opened to the public and other proposed changes. She ended with the new castle museum, hoping against hope that this would shake the baron from his sullen, uncommunicative state.

To her considerable relief it did, and she managed to start him talking about his plans for the various exhibits and about the new artefacts he had unearthed during his treasure hunt at the weekend. The others joined in with their own suggestions and when the baroness, in particular, mentioned diaries belonging to her husband which she had been keeping safe, the baron's eyes positively lit up. As a result he was in a more buoyant mood as lunchtime approached, so deciding that the time had come, Alice drew the meeting to an end and asked the million dollar question.

'Can I take it that I have your approval to engage the services of Luca Montorso? The sooner we can get an architect on the job, the better.'

All eyes turned towards the baron, and even the old grey cat raised its head from its position sprawled across Simonetta's lap. There was a pregnant pregnant pause before Simonetta's father gave a resigned nod of the head. 'So be it, but don't blame me if the mayor launches an all-out war.'

To the cat's chagrin, Simonetta stood up and went across to give him a hug. 'Well, if he does, we'll be ready for him. Don't forget we live in a castle, after all. Next time you go hunting for old artefacts, see if you can find a few muskets, or even a cannon or two.'

When Alice got back to her office, she sent a text message to Luca Montorso. It contained a short message telling him that the baron and the rest of the family had agreed to engage him, and asking him to contact her when he had a day and time for his first visit to the castle. His reply came through an hour later asking her to pass on his thanks to the baron and arranging to come on Wednesday morning. He told her he had things to finish before then but that he had earmarked the whole of Wednesday morning so he could take a good look around. She felt a little stab of disappointment that she was going to have to wait thirty-six hours to see him again, but she was quick to shake that off. He was coming on business, she told herself firmly, and she should stop behaving like a character in a fairy-tale romance. They hardly knew each other and, besides, she had a feeling that when he found about her prosthetic leg he would probably lose any possible interest in her he might be harbouring – just like Maurizio.

That evening, after she'd stopped off to buy provisions at the general store in the piazza and was emerging with a bag full of groceries, she spotted Silvia from the castle sitting at a table outside the bar, sipping what looked like a cooling lemonade. The sun had been shining non-stop all day and Alice felt sure the temperature must already be in the high twenties so she decided to stop for a cold drink as well. She had never liked the idea of sitting outside a bar by herself but, seeing as there was somebody here that she knew, she walked across to where Silvia was sitting.

'All right if I join you? Or are you waiting for some-body?'

Silvia blushed and made as if to stand up, but Alice laid a hand on her shoulder and pressed her back into her seat. 'Don't get up, please. I'm not the baron, you know.' She sat down alongside Silvia with her back to the wall, looking out over the square. 'Had a long day?'

Gradually the two of them started to talk, and once Alice had impressed upon her that she was just an employee rather than a member of the family, she sensed that Silvia began to relax a bit. Inevitably, the question of Simonetta's newfound – or at least newly revealed – boyfriend came up. It was clear that Silvia was dying to know who he was, but as Alice hadn't heard any more from Simonetta about when she intended to go ahead and tell her father all about it, she just shrugged her shoulders and pleaded ignorance. Instead, she enquired whether Silvia had a special somebody in her life and, once again, the woman blushed.

'Sort of...'

She was looking acutely uncomfortable and, remembering the exchange of glances between Silvia and Achille that she had intercepted, Alice had a feeling she knew why, but for now she was quick to jump in and move the conversation on with a platitude. 'Relationships can be difficult, can't they?'

'They really can. What about you, Alice? Have you left some man behind in England?'

Alice shook her head. 'No, I've had a few boyfriends over the years, but I still haven't found a keeper.'

'Simonetta said you used to work up north in the Dolomites. Surely there must have been a few handsome ski instructors up there?'

Maurizio had been an expert skier but because his family owned a hotel, he had worked there. Thought of him and the hurt he had caused her darkened Alice's mood, but she was delighted to find that she soon rallied. Progress indeed.

'There was one man, but he turned out not to be as good as he looked.'

Silvia must have heard the emotion in Alice's voice and she reached across with her hand and patted her on the arm. 'You'll find the right man, I'm sure. You're so pretty.'

Alice managed to smile back at her. 'Thank you, but nothing like as pretty as you. Somehow I doubt I'll ever find the right man.' She could have told Silvia the real reason why she had convinced herself she would never find the right man, but she chose to keep that to herself. The titanium and carbon prosthetic limb below her left knee was nobody's business but hers. But Silvia was no fool.

'I heard about your accident, but that's all in the past now, isn't it? You just wait. You'll find someone special soon.'

Alice almost blurted out that she might even already have found him but she decided it was best not to even think of Luca Montorso in that light – at least for now. 'Why don't you tell me about your man instead?' Alice changed the subject away from herself and tried giving Silvia another little prod about her own relationship status. This time she got a fuller answer, not complete disclosure, but a step in the right direction.

'There is a man.' Silvia glanced around apprehensively and lowered her voice. 'I've known him for years and I've probably been in love with him almost since the first day I saw him, but there's nothing going on between us and I know that nothing ever can happen.'

'How come? He's not married or something, is he?'

She saw Silvia blush again. 'No, he's not married, it's just that it's very complicated.'

If Silvia didn't want to mention Achille by name, Alice knew it wouldn't be right to press her any further, despite her suspicions. After all, she reminded herself, Silvia wasn't the only person here reluctant to divulge a secret. She did, however, offer a piece of advice. 'Why don't you tell him how you feel, or at least ask him out and see how you get on together? We're no longer in the dark ages, you know.'

Silvia shook her head. 'I couldn't possibly... Like I say, it's complicated.'

And that was all Alice could get out of her.

–

On Tuesday morning she had a visit in her office from Alfonso who brought interesting news.

'I've spoken to some of my farmer friends and apparently there's a man just on the other side of Salsomaggiore who keeps alpacas. His names's Silvestri and here's his phone number if you want to get in touch. He might have some animals to sell or, if not, he might know somebody else who has. If you're lucky, you might even be able to get some tips from him about keeping them.'

Alice thanked him and immediately gave the man a call. It rang a few times but then a voice answered. From the sound of it, he was an elderly man. '*Pronto.*'

Alice explained who she was and where she was calling from and that she was planning to set up a herd of alpacas and he expressed interest. In response to her request to visit, he sounded willing and she decided to strike while the iron was hot and go that same afternoon. Once the call had ended, she asked Alfonso if he would like to go with her and he nodded eagerly.

'Pietro can carry on repairing the fences without me. What time should we go?'

'How long's it likely to take us to get there?'

'If we go down the valley and take the main road, probably forty minutes or so. If we go through the hills, it's a few kilometres shorter, but it'll probably take us a little bit longer on the winding roads.'

The idea of driving through the foothills of the Apennines had considerable appeal to Alice so they decided to leave at two so as to be at the alpaca farm before three. It proved to be a most informative afternoon – and not just because of what Alice learned about alpacas.

On the increasingly narrow, tortuous road through the hills, she and Alfonso chatted and he proved once again to be a mine of information. For her part, as Luca Montorso would be seen and no doubt recognised by everybody when he came arrived next morning, she told Alfonso about him and the fact that he would be responsible for upgrading the castle into a tourist attraction. There was amazement, but also maybe a touch of something more, in Alfonso's voice when he responded.

'Well, well, well, who would've believed it? A Montorso working for the Varaldo family. I never thought I'd see the day. This has to be your doing, Alice, and if you don't mind me saying so, I'm very pleased and very impressed. I'm quite sure that without you this would never have happened. It's ridiculous that the feud's been running for so long. Here's hoping this marks the beginning of the end of it.' He paused for a few seconds. 'Although it all depends on how our illustrious mayor, Cesare Montorso, reacts to it, and I fear he won't approve one bit.'

Altogether, they spent almost an hour with the alpaca farmer who was very helpful, particularly when Alfonso discovered that his own sister-in-law and Signor Silvestri's uncle were in some convoluted way related. He took them into a field where there were probably thirty or forty alpacas grazing peacefully. Several of them came wandering over and appeared happy to be stroked and petted. Alice had a little smile to herself. They were certainly very different from those 'damn ostriches' at her father's farm. These docile animals looked similar to llamas, came in a whole range of colours from white to dark brown and appeared to have a permanent smile on their faces.

The good news was that Signor Silvestri told them he would be prepared to sell them a pair of his animals and he gave them contact details of other breeders from whom they should be able to buy more stock to build up their own herd. He also added a bit more advice.

'They're no trouble, and all you have to do is make sure they get sheared every spring or early summer. I can give you the names of people who could do that for you, if you like. You'll make reasonable money by selling the fleeces, but if you want to increase your profit, I'd advise you to go one or even two steps further.' In response to Alice's quizzical expression, he elaborated. 'Instead of selling the fleeces to a buyer who'll turn them into yarn, do that yourselves. It's not too complicated and you'll immediately double the value of what you have. And if you want to make serious money, start making your own woollens; you know, jumpers and scarves and so on. That's where the real money is. They're hypoallergenic and they sell for a premium.'

He showed them a little gift shop his wife had set up in an outbuilding and Alice bought herself an absolutely beautiful soft grey jumper that would no doubt help her keep warm over the cold winter months. It wasn't cheap but it felt wonderful to the touch and she told herself it would hopefully be a useful bargaining chip if the baron decided to go back on his agreement to farm alpacas. As an afterthought, she also bought a cosy scarf to give to Simonetta as a present.

In the car on the way home she discussed the project with Alfonso, and they both agreed that the castle would need to have a souvenir shop, and that this would be the perfect spot to start selling their own woollens. It turned out that Alfonso's wife had a cousin who lived just outside Prato in nearby Tuscany where she was involved in the knitting business. Apparently a cottage industry had grown up in some parts of Tuscany where people used knitting machines in their own homes to produce high class jumpers for local factories. Every week vans came around to collect finished garments and to deliver fresh wool. He told Alice he would get more information for her and she was delighted.

'Of course, the best people to talk to about knitting are Ines and her daughter, Silvia. They're both dead keen and they sell their stuff at the local farmers' market every spring and autumn.'

'That *is* interesting. I had a drink with Silvia outside the café on the square last night and she strikes me as being very bright. Maybe she might be the right person to look after that side of things and to run the gift shop?'

'I'm sure she'd leap at the chance. She's bright all right and I'm sure she'd be delighted. I imagine being a kitchen maid can get pretty boring.'

'I'm surprised she hasn't got herself a more interesting job already? Is it because she wants to be near her mum?'

'It's because she wants to be near somebody, but that somebody's not her mother.'

Although she felt sure she knew the answer, Alice shot him an inquiring look. 'I'm not following. Who does she want to be near?'

Alfonso began to look a little uncomfortable. 'I'm sorry, I was just repeating gossip. Forget I said anything, please.'

Alice respected his request and didn't press him further, but the more she thought about it, the more it made sense. She was increasingly convinced that Silvia's one true love that she had mentioned the previous day would turn out to be none other than Simonetta's big brother, Achille. Silvia had fallen in love with the future Baron Varaldo. Of course this would explain why she had convinced herself that nothing could come of her infatuation because of their different situations. It occurred to Alice that if the Varaldo family were prepared to employ one of their enemies as their architect, might they also be prepared to consider a marriage that crossed historic social divides? She would have dearly loved to know what Achille thought about this but, of course, this was a personal matter and there was no way she could ask him, or even his sister. Maybe with time…

Besides, she could hardly criticise Silvia for not disclosing her true feelings when she herself was harbouring her own secrets. Mind you, she thought to herself, having secrets appeared to be the name of the game here in Varaldo, for everybody – including herself.

Chapter 16

The Varaldo family's newly appointed architect arrived early on Wednesday morning. The clock in the village was just striking eight when Alice saw a car drive into the courtyard and park alongside her little Fiat. It was the silver sports car she had seen the previous month, this time with the top down. Inside it, two heads were visible: one human, one canine. She got up and went out to greet Luca Montorso and Frank the dog. The man gave her a little wave as she approached, and the Labrador jumped to his feet and put his paws up on the dashboard, his tail wagging energetically as he looked at her over the top of the screen.

'Good morning, Alice. Frank, get down! The car's scratched enough as it is. I'm afraid I forgot to ask if it was all right for me to bring Frank. Don't worry if it isn't. I gave him a walk on our way up here and he'll sleep happily in the car for a few hours.'

'Good morning, Luca. Thanks for coming. I would imagine it'll be fine for Frank to follow you around, but we'll ask Simonetta just in case. You know her, don't you?'

'Of course.' No doubt sworn to secrecy, he didn't mention the connection between Simonetta and his brother. 'And I know Achille as well from when we were kids, but there hasn't been much contact between us since then. I've never met the current Baron although I did meet his wife once. I liked her. She was a nice lady.'

He climbed out of the car, and the Labrador jumped out after him and came across to Alice's side to say hello. She was just bending down to stroke him when she saw Simonetta emerge from the front door and walk over to greet Luca. At the same time Alice couldn't help noticing the net curtains on her grandmother's window twitching. There was a strange, slightly embarrassed look on Simonetta's face as she held out her hand towards Luca, and Alice wondered if this meant she hadn't yet found the courage to break the news of her relationship with Tommaso to her father and was afraid he might be watching. Officially, of course, neither Simonetta nor her brother had had any contact with the Montorso twins since their schooldays.

'Good morning, Luca, I'm delighted you've said yes.'

'Hi, Simonetta, it's good to see you again.' Luca shook hands formally and it was clear that he, too, was on his best behaviour, and Alice almost giggled. He indicated Frank the dog. 'I hope you don't mind, but I brought my four-legged friend with me. If you'd rather not have a dog in the house, I can leave him in the car. It's not a problem.'

Simonetta bent down to pet Frank. 'The only objections might come from Baffo, our old cat, but he can always go and sleep on top of a cupboard.' She glanced up at Alice. 'Are you a dog person or a cat person, Alice?'

'I'm an all kinds of animals person – apart from snakes and a few creepy-crawlies.' She looked across at Luca. 'Frank doesn't sound very Italian, as names go.'

'I called him Frank after my hero, Frank Lloyd Wright; the greatest architect of the twentieth century... well, in my humble opinion anyway.'

'He's a big dog but he's not very old, is he?'

'Frank's not two yet, still a bit of a hooligan.'

Pleased to hear his name mentioned, the dog wandered around among the three of them, prodding them with his nose and wagging his tail lazily while Simonetta returned her attention to Luca.

'It's a bit early for the rest of the family, so why doesn't Alice show you around the cellars, the ground floor and the towers? I imagine by the time you've seen those, the others will be up and about, and I can introduce you to them. I'm really pleased that you agreed to come and do this for us. You have an excellent reputation and I know you'll do a great job.' She was still sounding very formal and Alice hoped that she would manage to break the news of her relationship with Tommaso to her father before too long.

After Simonetta had returned to the house, Alice looked across at Luca. 'Where would you like to start? Are you happy if I come around with you or would you prefer to be on your own?'

'I'm very happy to have you with me.' He sounded as if he meant it and Alice was furious with herself when she felt her cheeks flushing. The man was here to do a job and that was that – at least for now. She did her best to adopt a business-like tone.

'Shall we start at the bottom and work upwards? There are extensive cellars and stores and what were maybe dungeons beneath the main structure, so I'll take you there first if that's okay with you. Have you got a torch? It's pitch dark down there and there's no electricity. I'll just run and get mine.'

She went back to her office to get her torch and when she returned she found that he had retrieved a little back-pack, a torch and a clipboard from the car. They went in through the entrance hall and down the steps to the cellars, the Labrador trotting happily between the two of them. They spent over half an hour down there, hunting around with torches, and in the course of his explorations Luca discovered something that Alice had completely missed on her previous visits. It turned out that there were in fact yet more rooms beneath these cellars, accessed through a half-concealed trapdoor in the floor. He heaved the hefty wooden door open and she made her way gingerly down a narrow spiral stone staircase after him into the bowels of the earth, and was pleased to find that her knee managed it without complaint. From the festoons of low-hanging cobwebs it was clear that nobody had been down here for ages. It was pitch black, musty and, if she was honest, really quite scary. She was glad she wasn't on her own.

They emerged into another, narrower corridor, flanked by low doorways on both sides. From the iron bars on the doors and the rusting chains hanging from the walls, the series of dank cells down here had clearly had a far more sinister purpose than just acting as storerooms. Alice shivered as they walked about, not just because it was freezing down there. Certainly, if these cells were to be opened to the public, there would probably have to be some sort of age restriction to avoid scaring little children half to death.

When they reached the end of the tunnel they came across a wide round opening in the floor. This was clearly a well and Luca's powerful torch revealed what looked like crystal-clear water only about a metre beneath their feet and, from the way the light penetrated downwards, the well was certainly deep. Alice was just leaning over, peering down into the water, when there was a sudden movement right in front of her. She jumped back and bumped into Luca, almost dropping her torch into the water. She felt a strong arm encircle her shoulders to steady her and his voice at her ear.

'Looks like we're not the only inhabitants of this part of the castle.' He trained the beam of the torch on the spot where she had seen movement and revealed a large brown toad sitting there, studying them impassively. 'In all probability this little guy is descended from generations of toads going back centuries. He's probably got more claim to the property than the Varaldo family.'

Luca released his grip on her and she glanced up at him. Fortunately, in the shadows down here there was no way he would be able to see the colour that had leapt to her cheeks. 'Thanks for catching me. I've never been a fan of frogs and toads. I just hope there aren't any of his long slithery relatives down here.'

'No, I'm sure there aren't any snakes down here.' He was probably trying to sound reassuring, but she felt sure she could detect doubt in his voice and she shivered again.

Doing her best to dismiss thoughts of snakes lurking in the shadows, she assumed what she hoped would sound like a confident tone. 'If you've finished down here now, shall we head back up to the surface?'

'Of course. Anyway, finding a well is a real bonus. Even here in the hills, water's expensive and we need to take advantage of any natural resources we find. We should be able to set up a pumping system so as to use water from here, if not for drinking, then for the new toilets and so on. Every little helps.'

Even the dog seemed keen to get back up the steps again and Alice was hard on his heels. Luca was behind her with his torch and she realised as she climbed that this meant that his face was level with her bottom. The feel of his arm around her had been more than pleasant and now knowing that his eyes were probably on her was exciting. Like it or lump it, she couldn't ignore the fact that she found this man very appealing. Of course, she knew next to nothing about his private life and she had no idea how he might feel towards her. For all she knew, he might be married with half a dozen kids. Not for the first time, she reminded herself that theirs was simply a business relationship. If he really was as good at his job as she hoped, the last thing she wanted was to make things weird between them and maybe even run the risk of losing him from the project. In consequence, she told herself firmly to concentrate on the job and nothing more.

Easier said than done.

She was relieved when they emerged blinking into the daylight. The morning sun was shining brightly through the slit windows of the entrance hall, giving the dog ever-changing zebra stripes as he padded around sniffing these new surroundings. As for his master, if he'd been thinking about her the way she'd been thinking about him, there was no sign of it. He appeared to be solely focused on the job and she wondered for a moment whether he had already realised she was disabled and had lost interest as a result. It was a distasteful thought, but it was what she had been fearing for four long years now. She had always hoped she would meet that special someone sooner or later, but she had been under no illusions as to how that special someone would almost certainly react to her disability.

Apparently oblivious to her dark thoughts, Luca scribbled on his clipboard before coming up with a bit of interesting news.

'From what I could see down there on the lower level, we might even have a much earlier date for the castle than we thought. The official construction date is the late twelve hundreds, early thirteen hundreds, but I'm not so sure now. Did you notice that all the arches down there were round Roman arches, and generally speaking, that style of construction dates back to before the Crusades, so pre-twelfth century. I'll have to look into it more closely and maybe get one of my friends – he's a professor of archaeology – to come along and give his opinion, but it looks to me as though the lower levels could date back as far as the turn of the first millennium.'

Alice was impressed. 'That would make this castle a thousand years old. That's amazing, wait till we tell the baron. He's heavily into the history of the family and the castle, so I'm sure he'll be excited to hear that.'

'Thinking about it, I imagine we'll probably find that the lower levels belonged to an earlier structure which was replaced when this castle was built, but even so, it makes this one of the oldest surviving castles in Italy.' He gave her a little smile. 'That should be quite a good selling point, shouldn't it?'

She smiled back at him. 'Any more discoveries like that will be gratefully received.'

They walked out into the fresh air and began a tour of the ground floor of the castle. There were a number of huge double doors leading from the courtyard into what had no doubt once been stables, stores and pretty basic accommodation for the garrison back in the days when this was a functioning defensive fortress. The outside walls had few, if any, openings and the widest of these were arrow slits that even Baffo the cat would have struggled to squeeze through. The walls themselves were over three metres thick and it was easy to see why this place had allegedly never been taken by an attacking force. There were piles of junk everywhere, and Alice was idly wondering if there might be a scrap yard who would be prepared to take all the metal items away, when Luca and his dog suddenly disappeared into the middle of a particularly dense pile of rubbish. There were the sounds of something heavy being moved and then, seconds later, she heard his voice.

'Alice, I think you might like to see this.'

She could just make out his hand beckoning from behind a particularly unattractive large heap of detritus, so she tentatively started to squeeze between a vicious-looking piece of rusty agricultural machinery whose purpose she could only guess at and a torn old mattress, its horsehair stuffing spilling out onto the ground. As she was doing so, she couldn't help thinking to herself that if she were a snake looking for a nice warm lair, then in there would be just the ticket. Something moved close to her feet and she jumped as a warm body rubbed against her calf. A glance downwards provided reassurance.

'Frank, you frightened the life out of me! Please get out of from under my feet.'

Obligingly, the Labrador turned and headed off while she gritted her teeth and followed in his footsteps until she reached Luca.

He had cleared some of the junk and pulled the dusty canvas cover off an old car with a flat tyre. She could see it quite clearly. Although it was covered with a thick layer of dust and cobwebs, she realised that it was actually a rather smart, long black car with a convertible roof. She glanced at the front of the bonnet and saw that it sported a silver three-pointed star inside a circle. She recognised this emblem and turned towards Luca who gave her a smile.

'Ever seen one of these before?'

'Is it a Mercedes?'

'Mercedes Benz, that's right. Just give me a moment, would you? I need to check something out.'

While she and the dog continued to investigate the old car, Luca pulled out his phone and started searching. Alice dragged a few more bits of junk out of the way so that she could take a closer look. The paintwork had dulled with age, but the vehicle still appeared structurally sound. She managed to open the driver's door and saw that the leather interior was in remarkably good condition, considering that the vehicle was quite obviously very old. Dissuading the dog from climbing inside, she pushed the door closed again and turned towards Luca. The smile on his face was even broader now and she queried what was going on.

'What is it? What've you found?'

He looked up from his phone. 'Got it! This website's the biggest auction house in Switzerland and this looks very much like this car here.' He scanned through the text alongside the photos for a few seconds before looking back up at her again, his eyes gleaming. 'According to this, what we have here is a late nineteen thirties Mercedes Benz 320B cabriolet. I'm amazed it's been left here to rot. The one in Zurich…' He held the screen towards her and she saw a gleaming black car on display. '…Just look at how much it sold for.'

At first, Alice could hardly believe her eyes and she caught hold of his hand and pulled the screen closer to her face to be sure. There could be no doubt about it. The car in the picture had been sold for three hundred and seventy thousand Swiss francs.

'In case you're wondering, the Swiss franc and the euro are pretty much at parity nowadays.'

Alice looked up in amazement, the magnitude of the discovery still sinking in. Suddenly realising that she was still holding his hand, she released it, but she was so stunned by this discovery that her cheeks didn't even flush.

'Three hundred and seventy thousand euros. That's an awful lot to pay for a car.'

He introduced a note of caution. 'Obviously there'll be considerable expense to return this car to its original condition but, even so, it looks like the Varaldo family are sitting on a real treasure here.'

'This is amazing. I can't wait to tell them.'

The opportunity to break the good news to the family came at ten o'clock that morning. Luca was officially introduced to the other members of the family in the living room and Alice felt genuinely sorry for him at first. The expression on his face as Simonetta led him in there was probably not that different from what would have appeared on the faces of soldiers about to leave their trenches and go over the top in World War I. The baron was standing by the fireplace with his hands holding his lapels, looking for all the world as if he were King's Counsel about to address the judge to ask for the death sentence. His mother was sitting bolt upright in a chair beside him with a serious expression on her face. Sensing the tension in the atmosphere, even Frank the dog stopped halfway across the floor and cast an uncertain glance back at his master. Simonetta was quick to relieve the tension.

'Nonna, Papà, this is Luca Montorso and he's just made the most amazing discovery.' She went on to recount what Alice and Luca had just told her about the Mercedes in the courtyard store, and the atmosphere in the room underwent a complete metamorphosis. In a matter of seconds, smiles appeared on all the faces, and Alice heaved a surreptitious sigh of relief. The baron relinquished his formal stance and came across to shake Luca's hand, while his mother, helped to her feet by her grandson, stood up so that she, too, could greet Luca. She also produced a charming welcome speech.

'Signor Montorso... Luca, it's very good to meet you. On behalf of all our family, welcome to Varaldo Castle and congratulations on starting your period of employment with us on such a high note. We can't thank you enough.'

'That's very kind of you, Lady Varaldo, and you, *Barone*. I'm delighted to meet you and, to be completely honest, I never thought this day would come. As you can imagine, my brother and I were brought up to loathe and detest your family, and all because of an unhappy father, bitter about things that happened way back in the mists of time. It would be wonderful if this could be the beginning of the end of this senseless feud.'

On his grandmother's instructions, Achille went to look for a bottle of champagne and they all toasted the arrival of Luca and the wonderful discovery he had made. Ines, who served the wine, looked as though her eyes were about to pop out of her head, and Alice could well imagine her astonishment to see a Montorso in the house after all that had passed between the two families. For her part, Alice hoped that this new spirit of glasnost would extend to the other members of Luca's family. Silvia appeared a few minutes later with a plate of her mother's home-made biscuits and the dog was delighted to be handed one by Simonetta. Needless to say, it went down his throat without touching the sides. Alice smiled to herself. She knew Labrador gluttony so well.

They drank their champagne and the atmosphere became ever more cordial, especially when Luca told the baron that he believed he had found evidence that the castle might be even older than they had thought. A real conversation developed between the two men and Alice exchanged knowing looks with Simonetta as they saw the baron being animated and welcoming. Finally Luca asked if it would be in order for him to spend the rest of the morning looking around the castle in preparation for a full structural survey that he and his assistant would undertake early the following week. Depending on what this threw up, he told them he would prepare a detailed schedule of works to be carried out and, with their approval, he would embark on the tortuous process of obtaining listed building consent for all the works from the all-powerful *Belle Arti* authorities.

When asked by Simonetta for his estimate of how long this might all take, he warned them that he felt they should plan for a grand opening not before the end of the year, and maybe not until next Easter, depending on how long it took to get all the plans approved and the work completed. Simonetta looked disappointed but Alice was quick to offer some encouragement.

'In the meantime I propose we press on with clearing out the junk. Let's start in the storerooms and I'll see if I can find a firm with a digger to remove all the rubbish from the moat. Above all, we need to begin to work the land, particularly forestry and alpacas.'

'Alpacas?' Luca looked across at her in surprise.

'On my father's advice. He recommends we seriously think about establishing a herd. Let me tell you all about what I learnt when I visited an alpaca farm with Alfonso.'

She went on to report what she and Alfonso had been told, particularly with regard not only to selling the fleeces, but actually going through the whole process of spinning yarn and knitting articles for sale in their new gift shop. The suggestions were met with general approval and she was authorised to buy a dozen or so animals in the first instance. Finally, the meeting broke up and Luca returned to his surveying, this time accompanied by Achille, with whom he'd been exchanging nostalgic stories of their early school days. Suppressing a touch of disappointment that she wouldn't be with Luca, Alice went out in search of Alfonso to give him the good news.

It really felt as though things were on the move.

Chapter 17

On the way home on Friday, Alice saw a man outside the *municipio* sticking up posters. Out of curiosity she went over to take a look and received a surprise. The posters were announcing a local referendum to take place in exactly three weeks' time, but what was striking was the subject of the referendum. It required a straight yes/no answer to the question:

> *The town authorities believe that opening Varaldo Castle to the public is a bad idea which will negatively affect inhabitants. Are you in favour of allowing this potentially damaging new project? Vote NO on the 29th of June.*

Alice pulled out her phone and took a photo which she immediately sent on to Simonetta and Luca. She just added a one line comment:

And so it begins.

The following day, after a morning spent shopping, washing and ironing, she drove down to the stables where she had booked a couple of hours on Horace the horse. When she got there, she was surprised – and delighted –

to see a familiar car parked outside. It was a silver Porsche and sitting alongside it, scratching his ear with his hind leg, was Frank the Labrador. Recognising her, he came charging across and almost knocked her over with his enthusiastic greeting. Seconds later, his master emerged leading a handsome black horse by the reins. Luca saw her and smiled. He didn't look particularly surprised, and the thought crossed her mind that maybe he already knew she would be there. If so, might this mean that he had deliberately organised things so as to join her?

'Ciao, Alice. You going riding as well?'

'Yes, there's still a lot of the family's land that I haven't seen yet, so I thought I'd take a little ride up the hillside to see what's what. What about you?'

'Emilia's an old friend and Nero here's my favourite horse. I normally try to ride every Saturday but I've had a busy spell over the past few weeks and haven't been here for a while. I'm just glad to get out again. Want company?'

She did.

Today was less sunny and quite a lot windier. The hill-tops in the distance were swathed in cloud and Alice felt sure there was rain on the way but hopefully it would wait until later. They crossed the road onto Varaldo family land and followed the track that would become the main route for the tree fellers when they started to extract the timber. This morning, Rocco with the neck tattoo had emailed a detailed proposal for a joint venture which promised to make the family a good income with very little outlay and very little effort, assuming they approved it at Monday's meeting. Alice told Luca about this as they rode along, and he gave her a grin.

'It looks like between us, you and I have managed to pay for ourselves already. By the way, I had a word with a friend in Parma who has a garage specialising in classic cars. When I told him about the Mercedes, he said he reckons it might well be worth even more than we thought. Anyway, if the family agree, he's going to come and have a look at it, and he can give an estimate for returning it to *Concours d'elegance* standard.'

The track climbed steadily through the trees and, sheltered from the wind, the sweet scent of resin was heady. The Labrador trotted happily alongside the horses, clearly delighted to be out in the open air. At one point he shot off sideways into the trees, barking furiously, but he returned a minute later in response to a whistle from his master, panting from the chase. Luca explained to Alice.

'Squirrels. He can't stand them.'

'We have red squirrels here. They're gorgeous; I hope he doesn't catch them.'

'Not without a ladder, don't worry.'

They chatted about all sorts as they climbed steadily until they emerged from the woods onto open grassland. A vestigial track curled around the contour line and they followed this, speeding up to a trot and then a canter across the open land. It was exhilarating and Alice enjoyed being out here and being with Luca. After a while they reached the ruins of a little shepherd's hut and stopped to give the horses a rest. They sat down side by side on a convenient boulder protected from the wind by the old stone walls, and carried on talking.

There was no getting away from it: she had to accept the fact that the little ripples that shot through her when she was with him were sure signs of attraction. They sat and chatted about her life in England and his time working on ancient monuments in the hilly hinterland east of Naples, and she found she was able to relax in his company. As they talked she studied him surreptitiously and there was no doubt that she liked what she saw. Apart from looking good, he was friendly, articulate and she instinctively felt that she could trust him, or at least she hoped so. Of course, she reminded herself, she'd been attracted to Maurizio as well, but the accident had soured things irrevocably. A glance at Luca's left hand revealed no wedding ring but that didn't mean much these days. Still, she told herself, it was better than seeing one on there, wasn't it?

Inevitably, the conversation came around to the upcoming referendum in the town and Luca shook his head sadly. 'News of my appointment at the castle has reached my father, and this is his way of getting his revenge for what I'm sure he sees as an act of treachery. I spoke to my brother yesterday and he told me that the old man's livid. Apparently he was stomping around the farmyard kicking the chickens and he actually kicked one of them so hard he killed it. Pretty soon now he's going to be completely out of control. I just hope nobody gets hurt… including him.'

'Do you think he's going to win his referendum?'

Luca shook his head uncertainly. 'I honestly don't know. He and his cronies have been spreading a lot of scare stories, saying the town's going to be invaded by hordes of tourists, coaches will be blocking the roads, and chaos and confusion will reign. I'm sure anybody in the business community would welcome it, because it's bound to bring valuable revenue and employment opportunities to the town. As far as the don't-knows are concerned, I suppose it would be wise to come up with some sort of counter publicity.'

'When we were trying to get planning permission to increase the size of the car park at the manor back in England we took out adverts in the local newspaper and that helped a lot in generating support. Is there a local newspaper here?'

'That's an idea. Most people read the regional paper, the *Gazzetta*, and I sometimes play tennis with one of the editors who works in Parma. You could certainly advertise in there, but before you go spending money on adverts, why don't I give her a call and see if they might be interested in doing an article?'

'That sounds brilliant, but what if your father finds out you're behind it?'

'I can't see how he would, but so what? He made it clear to me years ago that he never wants to see me again, and the feeling's mutual, so what's the difference? I can get her to contact you and hopefully they'll send somebody to do a story with a photograph or two. Make sure she mentions the positive things like employment opportunities and helping to boost the status of the town as a prime historic site.'

They had a most enjoyable afternoon, even though persistent drizzle settled in for the last half hour as cloud descended from the hilltops to swathe the whole valley. Alice very nearly invited him around to her flat for a coffee afterwards but hesitated, wondering if that might be deemed unprofessional. However, before she could say anything he told her he had to scoot off as he was playing tennis. He didn't tell her anything about his tennis partner – in particular their gender – and she didn't ask.

But she spent all night wondering all the same.

–

On Sunday evening she went to the restaurant as usual, but there was no sign of Luca and his dog. Maybe Saturday's tennis match had led to dinner or more and had lasted all weekend, or maybe he was deliberately keeping his distance. Either way, she told herself, there was no point getting hung up on a man with whom she had to maintain a solid working relationship. Any emotional entanglement would only complicate things.

While this sounded very sensible and logical inside her head, it didn't make her feel any more cheerful.

A lot happened the following week. On Monday, Luca arrived with Carlo, his young assistant, but Alice barely had a chance to exchange more than a few words with him before the two men embarked on the survey. In all, although they were at the castle for two full days, she saw very little of him, and the idea that he might be deliberately keeping his distance kept nagging at her. As far as the survey was concerned, by the end of Tuesday Luca was able to pass on his initial conclusions which were reassuringly positive.

'Considering the age of the property, the castle's structurally sound. The roof was obviously completely replaced less than a hundred years ago and as far as I can see there's no rot of any kind in the timbers which is excellent. I've identified a few minor leaks, mainly around chimneys, but they shouldn't be any trouble for a roofer to sort out. There's a certain amount of making good of uneven floors and re-plastering of walls to be done, but generally speaking, I've been pleasantly surprised with how little work needs doing. I'll draw up the plans and produce a schedule of works and then we can start getting quotes from builders. I'll do that over the next few days so that we can prepare the submission to the authorities for permission to do everything. All in all, it's looking good.'

On a more personal level, all that Alice managed to get out of him was the arrangement to meet up for another ride on Saturday afternoon, but that didn't necessarily indicate that he wanted anything more than a riding companion. As she watched his car drive off, she felt a little pang of regret that she hadn't been able to spend more time with him and she wondered how next weekend might pan out.

Meanwhile, Alfonso had managed to locate another three pairs of alpacas and he was sent off in the Land Rover and trailer to collect them and bring them to their new home. Alice was there when the first of them arrived and her initial impression as these fluffy, delicate, long-necked sheep-like animals picked their way unsteadily down the ramp and into the field was one of immediate attraction. She was pleasantly surprised that they seemed quite happy for her to walk up to them and stroke them. Certainly, most sheep would never have let her do that. And as for her father's 'damn ostriches'...

She got Alfonso to take a photo of her with her arm around the necks of a pair of them and she sent it to her father with the caption, No pecking, no kicking, no aggression. Great idea, Dad. xx.

Next day there was a call from a woman at the *Gazzetta* in Parma who identified herself as the features editor. She said she had spoken to Luca and was interested in doing an article on the family's bid to open the castle to the public and told them she would send a reporter the following day. Sure enough, at ten o'clock on Thursday morning, Alice and Simonetta were visited by a young man, probably a few years younger than they were, accompanied by an elderly photographer. After taking a number of photos of the two of them, the photographer went off to get some shots of the castle accompanied by Silvia, while Alice and Simonetta sat down in the lounge to talk to the reporter. In all, they talked for about half an hour and the journalist appeared particularly interested in the fact that the civic authorities seemed to be so firmly against the development. By agreement, neither Alice nor Simonetta mentioned the feud between the two families as there was no point in further infuriating the mayor, and by the time the reporter left, they felt confident there would be a positive article in this Saturday's newspaper.

It was therefore with some anticipation that Alice went into the newsagents on Saturday morning and bought a copy of that day's paper. She took it into the café and sat down to read the article over a cappuccino. It came as a considerable shock to find that the young journalist the paper had sent had dedicated almost half of page three to the story – and what a story! The banner headline that ran right across the page read:

BLOOD FEUD RESURFACES AFTER 500 YEARS

Alice barely noticed the arrival of her coffee as she read and re-read the article several times. Along with a number of very good photos of the castle and one of Simonetta and herself in the living room, the article immediately homed in on the feud between the families, and Alice found herself wondering how they had found out. She wondered if Luca had said something but then quickly discovered that he hadn't been the origin of the leak after all. According to the article, it had emanated from none other than the owner of the establishment where she was currently drinking her cappuccino. She remembered that Luca had told her that there was no love lost between his father and Giorgio Chiesa here at the restaurant. Clearly, the journalist had headed for the café after Wednesday's interview at the castle and Giorgio had been only too happy to dish the dirt.

The article made it quite clear that in the opinion of the *Gazzetta*, a serious abuse of power was taking place and that this merited further investigation by higher authorities. It ended with a single line:

> We approached the mayor of Varaldo, Cesare Montorso, for comment but he was unavailable.

Alongside it was a photograph of Luca and Tommaso's father in his official regalia, no doubt taken from some ceremony he had attended in the past. Alice studied it carefully. This was the first time she had seen the face of the man she had come to think of as some sort of demon, and she was mildly surprised to see that he was a good-looking man sporting a friendly smile on his face. Unlike his sons, he had dark hair, but the family likeness in the cheekbones was clear to see.

She had just finished reading the article for the third time and was reaching for her now cold coffee when a shadow fell across the table and she looked up to see the restaurateur himself standing there.

'I see you've read it. Rather good, I thought.' There was a hint of a smile on his face.

'Wow, this is going to put the cat among the pigeons.'

Giorgio's smile was replaced by a scowl. 'It's about time somebody took him down. He's been getting far too big for his boots.'

'I just hope it doesn't make him even more extreme in his behaviour.'

Chapter 18

By the time Saturday afternoon arrived, the temperature had climbed into the high twenties. Alice met Luca and Frank at the stables as arranged and the first thing she did, after petting the dog, was to ask Luca if he'd seen the article in the paper. He nodded soberly.

'Tommi called me this morning. He said our father's been ranting and raving, and he stormed off into the *municipio* to call an emergency meeting of some kind. I must admit I wasn't expecting the *Gazzetta* to pick up this side of the story, and I feel sorry for Tommi as he's the one who's going to have to put up with my father and his tantrums.'

'What do you think your father will do?'

'What *can* he do? The article may make unpleasant reading to him, but it's only the truth. Everybody in the town knows it. Maybe getting it out in the open like this will be cathartic for him. Maybe it needs a jolt like this to make him realise just how crazily he's been behaving.' He shook his head regretfully. 'But I honestly don't know. I almost feel sorry for the man now after hating him for so long. I left home as soon as I finished school and I took a series of jobs to see me through university. There's no excuse for his treatment of the two of us, particularly

Tommi who could never stand up to him. And it was just as bad, if not worse, for my mother.'

'What made you decide to leave home, if you don't mind me asking? That's a major step.'

His expression hardened. 'There's a limit to the number of times you can stand being shouted at and threatened. As boys we had to work harder than the farmhands and for no pay. He was just permanently in a foul mood.'

'He treated you that badly?' Luca just nodded silently and Alice didn't know how to respond. 'I'm so sorry to hear that, Luca. No child should have to go through that.' Seeing the pain in his eyes, she tried for a more positive note. 'Well, like you say, maybe airing the whole subject will make him see reason. Now, it's a beautiful day and the sun's shining, so where are we going for our ride?'

He suggested they go in a different direction this time and she agreed willingly. To be honest, she didn't mind where they went as long as she was with him. The good news was that he appeared to be happy in her company so maybe he really had been very busy and hadn't been avoiding her. He led her out of the stables and onto a narrow track between two fields, heading back down the valley for a change. When the track widened enough for them to be able to ride side by side with the happy dog trotting ahead of them, Luca explained what he had in mind. Alice was pleased to see him smiling again. Hopefully the dark cloud cast by talking about his father had passed, at least for today.

'I thought you might like to see the Blue Lake. That's what we call it because of its intense colour. As kids, Tommi and I used to come down here very often in the summer to go swimming, but I haven't been back for a few years now. I hope it's still as beautiful as it used to be.'

It was.

After twenty minutes or so, a fast-running stream emerged from a steep sided gorge and joined the river they had been following down the valley. Luca led the way and turned onto a narrower path, heading up the gorge. They climbed steadily for about five or ten minutes, and the horses had to pick their way up what was little more than a goat track in single file, but they took the rocky terrain in their stride – literally. Just as it looked as though the gorge was about to close in on them, Alice heard the sound of rushing water and they emerged from the trees into a clearing. The Blue Lake was right in front of them and Alice reined in and stared at it in awe.

It wasn't very big – barely half the size of a tennis court – and almost completely circular. Hemmed in by steep rocky walls, it was fed by a narrow ribbon of water that emerged from the rockface ten metres or more above them and plunged down into the pool, sending countless tiny droplets of water into the air to sparkle in the sunlight, creating a multi-coloured mist of tiny rainbows. The water was crystal clear and she could see right to the bottom of the surprisingly deep pool, maybe three or four metres below the surface. A tiny gravel beach, just wide enough for the two horses to stand side by side while they leant forward to drink, was the only access, short of diving off the surrounding cliffs.

Following Luca's example, Alice dismounted, looped the reins around a low hanging branch and walked to the edge of the pool where she crouched down and scooped up a double handful of water. It was so cold, she almost squealed. At the same moment there was a thunderous splash and she looked over to see the dog's head emerge from the water with a big smile on his hairy face as he paddled happily about, looking more like a seal than a dog, and clearly in his element. Alice glanced up to where Luca was standing behind her with a relaxed smile on his face and she held her hands up towards him.

'The water's so cold I can feel it freezing my fingers. It's all right for Frank, he's got a fur coat, but are you telling me you really used to swim in this? You must be crazy.'

He grinned. 'I didn't say I still do. As kids, you don't feel the cold so much. Nowadays I come up here from time to time, but I wouldn't dream of going in the water again.' He pointed upwards. 'The water pouring down that waterfall comes straight out of the mountainside and it's the same low temperature all year round, two or three degrees above freezing. Even in the depths of winter, the flow never stops. Still, it's a lovely place, isn't it?'

Alice straightened up and looked around. He was right. This really was a beautiful spot and she couldn't help thinking that it was also a very romantic one. As the realisation dawned on her that she was here completely alone, apart from two horses and a dog, with a handsome man for whom she could easily develop feelings − maybe already had − her throat suddenly dried. Apparently unaware of her state of heightened tension, Luca slipped off his backpack and set it down on a boulder smoothed by millennia of rushing water. From the bag he produced a bottle of the same local Lambrusco she had tasted at the restaurant, two plastic wine glasses, and a little cardboard package that he opened to reveal a selection of delicious looking pastries. He held the bottle in the air.

'Feel like a drink?'

She nodded and grinned at him. 'Definitely. Tell me, is this the sort of picnic you always take with you on your rides, or is this a special occasion?' A sudden thought occurred to her. 'It's not your birthday, is it?'

'No, it's not my birthday, and I don't normally ride around with a bottle of Lambrusco on my back but, yes, this is a special occasion.'

She walked over and stood beside him. 'How special?'

'Very special. Mind out, after being shaken about on the way here, the wine's going to be pretty fizzy.' Sure enough, in spite of his best efforts to contain it, the cork came out with a loud explosion that startled the horses, and a fine mist of wine sprayed across Alice's face. As she wiped the drops from her cheeks, Luca shot her an apologetic look 'Sorry about that. Maybe fizz wasn't such a good idea after all.'

Alice licked the foam from her fingers and accepted a glass of remarkably cool wine from him. Once he had set the bottle down in the water by their feet, she tried again. 'You were going to tell me what we're celebrating.'

He held out his glass towards her. 'I'm not sure if it's something *you* want to celebrate, but for me, it certain— LOOK OUT!'

The next thing she knew, he had thrown himself across her and was holding her tightly to his chest, both of them struggling to avoid dropping their wine glasses. There was the sound of splashing followed by the unmistakable noise of a large dog shaking himself dry. Moments later, Luca released his hold on her and jumped back, pointing down at her in dismay.

'I'm so sorry, I stepped on your foot. I haven't hurt you, have I?'

Alice glanced down and saw the outline of his boot still distinguishable on the top of hers. He must have landed on her with some force while trying to shield her from Frank's unwelcome shower, but she hadn't felt a thing. The reason for this was that there was no foot inside this boot. She stood there for a second or two, wondering if this might be the moment to tell him about the accident and its consequences, but things had been going so well between them this afternoon that she decided to wait, rather than risk spoiling the mood.

'Didn't hurt a bit. Don't worry about it. Thank you for keeping the water off me.' She gave him a smile and sat down on the boulder. 'And they say the age of chivalry's dead. Look at you, you're soaked!' She came close to suggesting he take off his shirt and hang it up to dry in the sunshine, but she stopped herself in time. There was a limit to the amount of self control a girl could muster, after all.

He smiled back at her. 'I'm sorry about that. I should have seen it coming. Anyway, hopefully I managed to keep most of the water off you.' He sat down alongside her but not touching her. She was feeling distinctly rumpled, but not unhappy – very much the opposite. At their feet the unrepentant dog sat down in front of them and subjected the box of pastries to a covetous stare, while his master did his best to wipe a tsunami of Labrador-scented water off his shirt.

She waited until he had relaxed once more before returning to her original question. 'So, what's the cause for celebration?'

For a grown man he suddenly looked remarkably sheepish. She had to wait several seconds for his reply and when it came it surprised her. 'I'm celebrating the fact that this is the first time I've ever brought a woman here, and a very beautiful one as well.'

Now she was the one to look embarrassed. She could feel the colour rush to her cheeks and did her best to reply in a reasonably normal tone. 'Thank you for the kind words, but I'm surprised you haven't brought any of your lady friends here before.' They were getting into much more personal territory now, and she felt a return of the nervous tension.

He shook his head. 'No, you're the only one.'

There then ensued a long silence that he filled by replenishing their glasses which had both lost half their contents when Frank the dog had emerged from the water and shaken himself. Finally, Luca took a big mouthful and turned towards her again, still with that same uncomfortable expression on his face.

'This has always been a very special place for me. My mother used to bring Tommi and me here to get away from my father when he was in one of his moods. Some of my happiest memories are of splashing around in the water.' He drained the last of the wine in his glass before continuing, his eyes now staring out over the water towards the waterfall. 'I'm pleased to be able to share it with you.'

Alice reached over and laid her hand on his forearm for a moment. 'I'm very touched that you've brought me somewhere that means so much to you. Thank you so much.'

The intimacy of the moment was interrupted by a yelp from the ground in front of them as Frank made clear that he didn't feel he should be made to wait much longer for a pastry. His intervention broke the spell, but Alice didn't mind. The thought going round and round in her head was that Luca liked her enough to bring her here to his special place and that he had described her as beautiful. That had to mean something, didn't it? Whether he would still think she was beautiful when he knew all about her remained to be seen.

With a shrug of the shoulders and a resigned sigh in the direction of his dog, Luca picked up the box of little pastries and held it out towards her. Frank's eyes followed it all the way. There were a dozen or so assorted little profiteroles, fruit tarts, tiny chocolate cakes and a handful of biscuits in there, and Alice couldn't help smiling.

'Say what you like about Frank, but he knows a good thing when he smells one. These look absolutely gorgeous.'

She helped herself to a white chocolate profiterole and looked on as Luca selected one of the plain biscuits from the box and passed it down to his dog. It disappeared in a flash. Alice, on the other hand, took her time and nibbled the delightful, sweet pastry while she collected herself and reflected on how pleased she was that it looked as though Luca really liked her. It now remained to be discovered whether this was as much as she liked him.

And whether he still would, once he knew her secret.

They chatted easily about generalities and even about work, rather than anything more personal, but Alice did her best to relax in his company and in these beautiful surroundings. If it hadn't been for what she still had to tell him, it would have been perfect. By tacit agreement neither of them made any further mention of the newspaper article or his father, and the mood was comfortable and familiar. She felt as if she'd known him for years. Another glass of fizz and a couple more of the gorgeous little pastries completed the magical atmosphere as she readied herself to tell all. He really couldn't have arranged it better and she compared it to some of her other first dates – if this was indeed a date. These had included a sci-fi movie followed by a curry, a fifteen-mile hike across Dartmoor into the teeth of a winter gale, and dinner with Maurizio in his father's restaurant with his evil twin sisters scrutinising her every move. Yes, this was far more relaxing and satisfying.

Her reminiscing was interrupted by the sound of his voice.

'I don't suppose you'd like to come out for dinner with me tomorrow night? There's a super restaurant I know just a little way down the valley from here. Although we're in Emilia-Romagna, it has a Tuscan chef and the food there's really great.'

'I'd love that, thanks. I've never been to Tuscany but I've heard that Tuscan food's really good.' Her heart soared. This dinner invitation was unmistakably a date. She took a deep breath and braced herself. Now that it looked pretty clear that he was interested in her, she knew that the time had come to reveal her secret and risk the consequences. She was about to open her mouth when his phone started ringing. He gave her an apologetic glance and reached for it.

It was a short conversation but from what she could hear from his part it was clear that work had intervened, and when the call ended, she saw him glance at his watch regretfully. 'I'm sorry, I was hoping these people would cancel as it's the weekend but I've got to go and see them after all. They have a rather fine old stone house just to the east of Parma that they want to extend, so I'm afraid we'd better head back to the stables.' He reached for the remains of their picnic and started pushing them into his backpack. 'I'm really sorry. This was lovely, but I can pick you up at seven-thirty tomorrow night if that suits. Hopefully we won't have any more interruptions.'

Alice realised that the moment had passed and she just smiled back at him. 'That sounds great.' Her story would have to wait until tomorrow.

When she got back home, she stayed in, did some ironing, and spent most of the time with a silly smile on her face. It had been a perfect afternoon – well, the only thing that could have made it more perfect would have been a declaration of undying love from him. Somehow she felt more at home with him and here in Italy. Her only lingering regret was that she hadn't been able to summon up the courage to tell him about her leg.

She decided she needed to talk to somebody she knew well and it occurred to her that she hadn't spoken to Fenella since a brief call a couple of days after arriving in Varaldo, during which she had repeated her thanks to them for finding her this job. Fenella knew all about the accident even if she didn't know about Maurizio, and she had a sensible head on her shoulders. So at six o'clock Alice made herself a cup of tea and sat down with the phone. It rang a few times before it was answered by Fenella, accompanied by a chorus of yapping from Gladys the poodle in the background.

'Alice, hello, how lovely to hear from you. Gladys, do be quiet! How're things?'

'Things are really good, thanks.' Alice went on to tell her friend in some detail how everything was progressing on the work front and how she appeared to have been accepted by the family as one of their own. Fenella expressed considerable satisfaction and then asked a question of a more personal nature.

'Have you met any hunky Italian men yet?' There might even have been a note of longing in Lady Fitzgerald-Chagleigh's voice. 'You know, one of those tall, dark and handsome ones with a spaghetti farm and a gondola?'

Alice giggled. 'There wouldn't be much use for a gondola up here in the hills, but seeing as you're asking, yes, I *have* met a man, but he's got fair hair and he's an architect. I'm sure he eats spaghetti but I doubt if he grows it. Will he do?'

'Ooh, how exciting. Go on, tell me all about him.'

Alice produced a description of Luca and explained how they had met. She then went on to describe his toxic family relationship and how he and his father hadn't spoken for ten years. Fenella sounded as amazed as Alice that a father could have mistreated his children in that way.

'I wonder if he's always been like that. Hasn't he got a wife to keep him in order?'

'She left him some years ago when she couldn't stand the abusive behaviour any longer. According to Luca, he's been getting more and more extreme as the years go by. As he's the mayor I'm going to have to go and meet him one of these days and I'm not looking forward to it.'

'Well, remember what my father told me before I was sent off to boarding school at the age of eleven. There's only one way to deal with bullies and that's to stand up to them. By the sound of it, Luca has already worked that out for himself.'

Alice went on to tell Fenella about her visit to the Blue Lake with Luca and she heard cooing noises from the other end of the line.

'Your Luca sounds like the perfect man for you: bright, handsome, romantic and he even likes horses. You hang onto him.'

Alice felt she should sound a note of caution. 'He's not my Luca yet.'

'But I've a feeling he soon will be.'

'I wish I shared your confidence.' Alice took a deep breath. 'The thing is, I haven't told him about the accident… about my leg.' She went on to tell her friend how worried she was about his possible reaction when he found out that she was disabled, and how she had been delaying telling him, even after he had inadvertently stepped on her foot.

Fenella answered firmly. 'Don't be silly.' She knew all about Alice's fears and had been offering encouragement for years now. 'Now, don't you go getting all hung up about that all over again. It sounds to me as if he really likes you, and if he does, he'll accept you just the way you are, warts and all.'

They chatted for a while longer, and as much as Alice felt buoyed by Fenella's positivity, it wasn't enough to completely allay her concerns or fears. Would Luca really be accepting of her disability?

Chapter 19

On Sunday morning, Alice got a call from her mum. They had a good catch up in which Alice recounted pretty much what she had told Fenella last night and received the same sort of response, particularly when Alice talked about Luca.

'That's wonderful news. It's about time you found yourself a man. And a nice one. Not a slimy rat like Maurizio was.'

Alice felt duty bound to protest. 'I've been very happy up till now without a man, and I probably would have been quite happy without one for the rest of my life, but now you come to mention it, it does feel rather good.'

'Do you think it's going to get serious?'

'It's still early days, Mum. I'm taking it one step at a time.'

'But you'd like it to become more serious?'

Alice couldn't help giving an honest reply. 'Yes, I would, but like I say...'

'Yes, I heard you, you're taking it one step at a time. Well, I think it's marvellous. Hang on, your father wants a word.' There was a rustling noise and then Alice heard her father's voice.

'Hello, sweetheart. I'll get all the news from your mum but I just wanted to pass on a bit of information I picked up at the livestock market the other day. I've been meaning to call you. You know your alpacas? Well, I was talking to Reg Bolton who farms up in North Devon, and he was telling me he's got a herd of thirty alpacas and he's doing good business renting them out for walks or as guards.'

Alice struggled to wrap her head around what her dad had just told her. 'Renting them out for walks? Alpacas as guards? What on earth do you mean, Dad?'

She heard him chuckle. 'Apparently they're excellent guards against foxes, really plucky. He says he rents out a couple of pairs to neighbouring sheep farmers and they really earn their keep at lambing time. They just graze happily with the flock but if foxes come along the alpacas see them off. But he says the real money's in the walking.'

'Not following you, Dad. You'll have to explain.'

'He said that he's got a thriving business for people to come along, rent an alpaca for an hour or two, and take it for a walk in the country around where they are.'

'When you say a walk, do you mean that they ride them? They aren't that big.'

'No, apparently people are just happy to wander around the paths and fields with an alpaca on a lead.' His voice made clear his scepticism. 'I suppose it's city folk mainly, getting away from all that big business stress and the like. But I thought as you're opening the castle to the public, you could add alpaca walks as an extra attraction.'

'Amazing. We live and learn. Sounds like a good idea, Dad, thanks a lot.'

Alice learnt something else a couple of hours later. Around mid-morning she was just sitting down with a cup of coffee after planting courgette and tomato seedlings in her little piece of garden, when there was the sound of a vehicle outside and she saw that it was the Land Rover. She opened the door and gave Simonetta a wave.

'Feel like a coffee, or tea, or something else?'

'Hi, Alice, coffee would be great.' Simonetta came in and sat down at the kitchen table. As Alice made the coffee, she shot a couple of glances at Simonetta, but was unable to identify the expression on her face. Her mouth was smiling but her eyes were serious. Alice couldn't wait to find out what she had on her mind. She didn't have long to wait.

'I finally drummed up the courage to tell my father about Tommi this morning. I had to come and tell you.'

'I've been wondering when you'd get round to it. And how did he take the news?'

'Remarkably well. In fact, suspiciously well. I've been thinking about it on my way down here now and I have a feeling that Nonna might have got to him first. She may not have told him the full story, but I definitely sensed that he'd been primed. Somehow, I don't think it came as a complete surprise to him.'

'When you say, "remarkably well," how well? Did he try to talk you out of it or did he give you his blessing straight off?'

Simonetta took a sip of coffee before replying. 'I wouldn't say he tried to talk me out of it, but he did query whether I was sure I was doing the right thing. When I told him we loved each other and hoped to get married before too long, he actually got quite emotional. It was very sweet, really.'

'That's terrific news. I'm so happy for you both. I went riding with Luca yesterday and he was telling me about the way his father used to mistreat him and his brother. Thank goodness your father's a much gentler, more understanding sort of man.'

Simonetta looked up and there was a hint of a smile on her face. 'Getting Luca to open up about his private life is impressive. It's more than I've ever been able to do. I've been watching you two and I thought there might be something there. Are you seeing him again?'

Alice nodded. 'He's actually taking me out for dinner tonight.'

Simonetta's eyes opened wider and her smile broadened. 'So he's taking you on a date, that's terrific. Tommi tells me he hasn't seen him with a woman for ages. He just works and works and works.' Her expression became more serious. 'Do you see it going anywhere?'

'You sound like my mum.' Alice grinned to rob her words of any offence. 'To be honest, I like him a lot, but tonight will be our first real date – if that's what it is. I know the way I feel about him and hopefully I'll find out over the next few days and weeks how he feels about me.'

'It's such a pity that the shadow of his father hangs over him just like it does over Tommi. The referendum's coming up a week on Friday and after yesterday's newspaper article I've a feeling Cesare Montorso might be going to try some of his dirty tricks.'

'Well, just remember what you said to your father: you live in a castle and there's not much the mayor of a little town can do against a fortress with walls three metres thick.'

'Here's hoping.' Simonetta raised her cup in a little toast. 'And here's wishing you well on your date tonight.'

When Luca arrived to pick Alice up that evening she surreptitiously checked him out on the doorstep and was relieved to see him wearing jeans, so evidently he wasn't taking her to a dressy kind of place, which had been her main concern. As ever, she was wearing jeans – clean, smart and white, but still jeans. She hadn't worn a skirt or shorts since the accident. Luca's hair was freshly washed; he was looking good, and he even smelt good. While she petted the dog – who didn't smell quite as good – she felt Luca's eyes on her.

'You're looking great.' He sounded as if he meant it.

'And you're looking good too.'

A slightly awkward pause then ensued before he pointed at the car. 'Shall we go? By the way, the place I've chosen is happy to accept dogs, so our four-legged friend's coming with us.'

There was a narrow space behind the seats of the Porsche where Frank perched happily, and for the duration of the journey she and Luca had to put up with the excited dog breathing down their necks and nuzzling their hair, but she didn't mind. She and the Labrador were fast becoming bosom buddies – and hopefully soon the same could be said about his master.

As Luca drove back down the hill they chatted, and she asked him where he lived.

'Just outside Parma. I have a top-floor apartment in an old building. It's not huge but it's comfortable and it has a loggia.'

'How wonderful.' Alice had heard about loggias. These were covered terraces where people could take shelter from the sun but still get the benefit of the breeze in the oppressively hot summer months. 'With your Porsche, I had you pegged for a slick penthouse somewhere with bright lights and a bit of excitement.'

She heard him laugh. 'No, give me the quiet life any time. I'm a country boy at heart.' She saw his face turn towards her for a second. 'Parma's not the biggest city in the world but it's still too big for me. If it wasn't for my father I'd be back here like a shot. As far as this car's concerned, it was a gift from Mario, a guy I used to work for.'

'Wow, he sounds like quite some employer if he was giving out Porsches to his employees.'

'He and his wife didn't have any kids of their own and they sort of adopted me when I left home and went to work with them to pay my way through university. All right, I was eighteen, but like I say, I'm a country boy and I was quite lost in the big city at first. I owe them a lot. He gave the car to me when I graduated. It was twenty years old then and not exactly playboy transport, but it was amazingly generous of him.' She heard him give a frustrated sigh. 'Why couldn't my own father be somebody like that?'

After five or six kilometres, he turned to the left onto a narrow, winding road and they started to climb up a series of hairpin bends until they were high above the valley floor. The restaurant was in a delightful little village on the hilltop and their table was outside on the terrace, sheltered from the setting sun by the building itself. From here they had a spectacular view down towards Parma in the distance, and Alice could pick out the unmistakable shapes of the cathedral and the octagonal baptistery in the centre. Disappearing into the haze beyond the city were the sprawling flatlands carpeted with factories that made it one of the most productive areas in Europe, producing everything from luxury cars to some of the most famous foods in the world. In spite of being so far out in the country, the restaurant was almost full, evidently very popular, and the atmosphere animated.

They both chose mixed antipasti to begin with, followed by a grilled *bistecca alla fiorentina*. The waiter tried to persuade Alice to have a plate of pasta between the starter and the main course but she shook her head. Luca had been telling her about the legendary Florentine steaks that were the speciality of the house and she had no illusions as to the mountain of food that awaited her. At his suggestion, they ordered a bottle of ice-cold rosé that turned out to be excellent. He told her it was made locally and she nodded appreciatively. 'I'm definitely going to add this one to my list of fine local wines.' She pulled out her phone and took a photo of the label before clinking her glass against his. 'Thanks for this; eating on your own can get a bit boring after a while.'

He caught her eye. 'I'm kind of surprised you're on your own. How come a gorgeous, bright, talented woman like you is all alone? I would have thought you'd be fighting the men off.'

She did her best to ignore the compliments and shook her head. 'I've had a few relationships over the years, but none that amounted to anything, and nothing recently.' Once again she ducked out of the chance to tell him what had happened to her – and she certainly wasn't going to mention Maurizio. 'To be honest, this is just about the first time for ages I've been out one-to-one with a man.' She was interrupted by the arrival of their antipasti.

This consisted of a plate of thick slices of white bread topped with chopped tomatoes soused in olive oil, alongside a huge wooden board groaning with mortadella, salami and, of course, ham. In separate little dishes were artichoke hearts, sundried tomatoes and olives, all soaked in more of the wonderful thick olive oil, so fresh it tickled the throat. Alongside was a little salad made of sliced porcini mushrooms, covered in slivers of Parmesan cheese and yet more oil. It looked and smelt excellent. Alice glanced across at Luca and smiled.

'This looks wonderful. Thanks again for bringing me here.'

'Thank you for coming with me. I love it out here on the terrace, watching the shadows lengthen and the lights of the city gradually start to turn on. It's idyllic… and quite romantic.'

She had to agree with him on that.

They chatted about everything from walking with alpacas to Simonetta's big news about her father's acceptance of her choice of boyfriend, and the conversation flowed easily – as long as it didn't take a more personal turn. As far as telling Luca about her accident was concerned, the moment had passed for now, but she resolved to return to it as soon as it felt right. She could almost hear Fenella's voice echoing in her ears telling her to just tell him and be damned. The trouble was that she was terrified at the thought of what his reaction might be, so once again, she bit her tongue and said nothing. In a moment of self-awareness, she reflected that being so reticent bore an uncanny resemblance to Simonetta's reluctance to mention her relationship with Tommi to her father. It was fear of how the other would react. Things were going so well, it seemed foolish to risk spoiling everything, and Alice wasn't sure how she'd handle it if her fears were realised.

When they had eaten enough antipasti, a waiter came to remove their plates and then returned with an even bigger wooden board on which was a huge T-bone steak, the size and thickness of a bible, served with a pile of little roast potatoes flavoured with rosemary. The enticing aromas reached down as far as the dog. Alice heard a movement from under the table and then felt a heavy black nose land on her thigh. A pair of doleful brown eyes looked up at her adoringly or, more probably, greedily. She couldn't resist – and it also got Frank's nose off her clean white jeans – so she picked up a breadstick, handed it down to him and saw him subside back under the table with it. Luca had been observing the scene and he shot her a grin.

'Sorry about that, he knows I don't give him food from the table, but he always tries it on with everybody else. But you can't blame him, it does smell good.'

'Good? It smells and looks amazing, and I bet it tastes even better.'

And it did. Unbidden, the waiter proceeded to carve the steak away from the bone and then cut it vertically into slices, onto which he heaped more shavings of Parmesan, fresh rocket, and olive oil. He laid a fan of slices on each of their plates, added a little pile of potatoes and retired, promising to put the bone in a bag for the dog to devour when he got home.

Alice smiled across the table at Luca. '*Buon appetito* and thank you again.'

'You're most welcome. I couldn't ask for more charming company – and I'm not referring to Frank.'

She studied him over the rim of her glass. With his blue eyes, his broad shoulders and his strong, stubbly chin, he was without doubt a very attractive man. She took a sip of wine before replying.

'I couldn't ask for better either.' His eyes locked with hers as he smiled back at her.

The meal was excellent and then, as she was sitting back, digesting her wonderfully light *panna cotta* with raspberries and sweet raspberry syrup, he said something that since her conversation with Simonetta that morning didn't come as a complete surprise.

'Want to know something? This is just about the first time I've been out with a woman for a long time.'

'Really? I thought you'd be much more sociable than me. If you don't mind me copying what you said earlier, how come a handsome, bright, talented man like you is alone?' She caught his eye and grinned. 'I would've expected you to have a very active social life.'

'Nope. Like I said, I'm just fine on my own.'

Alice realised he still hadn't answered her question about why he was on his own, but she didn't press him, although she would be lying to herself if she said she wasn't interested in knowing the answer. There was no doubt about it, however: a serious tête-a tête was looming – whatever the result.

'This is going to be another very busy week for me,' Luca murmured, the restaurant quieter now as various tables had left for the night. 'Now that I've finished drawing up all the plans for the castle and I've submitted the outline proposal to the authorities, I really need to get back to the other jobs that I put off so I could come to the castle straightaway. This means I'm afraid I won't be around much for the next few days. I don't know what you're doing next weekend but I have to be in Milan on Saturday so I won't be able to come for a ride with you. On the Sunday, I'll be visiting an old medieval tower. It's a bit further to the west of here, high up in the Apennines near the skiing resort of the Abetone and it's in a very lovely spot. I was wondering if maybe you'd like to come with me. That way you can say that you've not only eaten Tuscan food, but you've also actually been to Tuscany, although we'll only really be just over the border. I've been responsible for the renovation works to the tower, and the inspector from the *Belle Arti* is due a week on Monday, so I thought I'd drop by to check that everything's in order. Maybe you'd let me buy you lunch that day. There's a really nice restaurant I know that I'm sure you'd like.'

Her disappointment that she was going to have to wait a full week before seeing him again quickly dissolved at the realisation that he had put so much thought into making sure he *could* see her again. 'I'd love to, but couldn't I at least buy you a meal in return?'

He grinned. 'We can argue about that next week.'

When the time came to walk back to the car, night had fallen and the sky was completely cloudless and a deep velvety blue colour. The near-full moon looked huge and she could even make out the larger craters just with the naked eye. He was dead right about this being a romantic place. Just before arriving back at the car they had to pause as Frank stopped to sniff and mark a battered copper drainpipe and she finally decided the time had come. As she stood there in the moonlight, searching for the right words to reveal her secret to Luca, she felt his hand grip her shoulder, turning her gently towards him. She didn't resist and could feel her eyes closing in readiness for his kiss when to her surprise he pointed upwards.

'Look, see that bright object just above the horizon? That's the International Space Station. Just think, there are people up there right now, looking down at us. It's an amazing thought, isn't it?'

By this time Alice's eyes were wide open again and she was relieved they were well way from the streetlights so, hopefully, he hadn't spotted her faux pas.

'Rather them than me. I think I'd better keep my feet on the ground.'

And her secret to herself for tonight.

Chapter 20

Next morning there was the usual Monday meeting with the family and, predictably, the main topic of conversation was the article in the *Gazzetta* and the question of how the mayor was likely to respond. Alice had asked Luca the same thing the previous night and he had shrugged his shoulders.

'I honestly don't know, but I'd be surprised if he doesn't try something to get back at the Varaldo family.'

'What sort of something?'

'I really don't know. Maybe Simonetta can try asking Tommi.'

'He's not going to do something stupid, is he? I mean, he wouldn't try and physically assault the baron or Simonetta or somebody up at the castle?'

'I certainly hope not, but I just don't know the man anymore. From what my brother told me, he was incandescent about the newspaper article and he's been getting ever more erratic in his behaviour, so I suppose anything's possible.'

When Alice recounted this to the family on Monday morning, she was impressed by their reactions. The baron frowned pugnaciously and snorted, while his mother – all five foot nothing of her – put her defiance into words.

'Just let him try. We're not living in the Middle Ages any more. If he did threaten any of us, I'd be on the phone to the police like a shot. We live in the twenty-first century and the rule of law will always prevail.' To reinforce her point, she thumped her little fist on the table so hard it woke Baffo the cat.

Simonetta and her brother looked equally determined, although Simonetta added regretfully that she had spoken to Tommi but that he had no idea what, if anything, his father might be planning. He had, however, confirmed that his father was still incensed; so incensed that Tommi had decided to delay telling him about his relationship with Simonetta and he asked them all to keep the secret for now. Once again, Alice felt sorry that things were so tough for him, and like the others, she promised Simonetta that their secret would be kept for as long as he wished. Nevertheless, Alice felt they should at least attempt some sort of rapprochement with the mayor.

'With your approval, I'd like to go and meet him face to face. I'd be happy to try to act as a sort of neutral intermediary. Would that be all right?'

'You'd do that?' Achille looked astonished. 'Why would you want to get involved with our troubles?'

'Because they're my troubles as well now. You've all been so kind and welcoming and I feel great sympathy for this family. Besides, as castle manager, I believe it's my job to go and see if I can pour a bit of oil on these troubled waters. What's the worst that could happen? He's hardly going to physically assault me.'

Simonetta reached over and caught hold of Alice's forearm. 'That's very sweet of you, but I'm afraid you'd just be wasting your time.'

'From what I've been hearing, I imagine you're probably right, but I'd like to give it a go if you all don't mind. I'm curious to see this man who sounds like a hang-back to the Dark Ages.' She produced a little smile for the benefit of the room. 'Please let me go, just so I can satisfy my curiosity, if nothing else.'

After receiving their reluctant agreement, she proceeded with the agenda and told them what her father had said to her about the versatility of alpacas, which raised a few smiles. She then informed them that Luca's friend, the classic car expert, would be coming the following day to cast an eye over the old Mercedes. 'He says it might even be worth more than we thought.'

She went on to let them know that an expert on antique furniture, old books and other precious items would be coming on Wednesday, but the baron immediately added a caveat.

'But I really don't want to sell anything that can go into the castle museum. Let's wait and see how much this car man thinks the Mercedes might be worth. If it's a decent amount, I'd like to avoid selling too many of our family heirlooms. Our thanks to our new architect...' He smiled across at Simonetta. '...my daughter's boyfriend's twin brother, who found this treasure we didn't know we had.'

At the end of the meeting, Alice called the town hall and asked if she could make an appointment to see the mayor. She was told in no uncertain terms that he was a very busy man, but when she mentioned her job title and the name of her new employers, the tone changed. She was asked to hold for half a minute and when the telephonist came back on the line it was with confirmation that an appointment had been made for that same day at noon, in less than two hours' time. Although nervous, Alice was looking forward to meeting Luca's father for the first time and to discovering how awful the man really was.

She walked up to the little house in the woods at eleven where she found Alfonso and Pietro. Accepting a cup of coffee – which surprisingly didn't appear to have anything sinister floating in it, at least at first sight – she told them what her dad had said about alpacas and, for once, it was Pietro who spoke up.

'They were talking about that on the TV only the other day. There was a report on a farmer up north near Asti who's offering walks with alpacas, and he was saying that they're very popular.' He looked up from his coffee and caught Alice's eye. 'And not just with kids.'

Alice tried to digest the fact that this was the longest single sentence she had ever heard from the taciturn giant while also digesting a suspicious lump of something she had just swallowed in her coffee. After taking another sip to wash down whatever it had been – and a silent prayer that it had at least been dead – she gave Pietro a big smile.

'Quite a few places in England offer that sort of thing nowadays. Apparently lots of stressed executives go walking with alpacas as a way of finding inner peace – that's the expression they use. There's a lot of industry around Parma, Bologna and Modena, so I imagine that means there must be lots of stressed executives here in this part of Italy as well. We'll have to see if we can get local TV interested.' A thought occurred to her. 'I have an appointment with the mayor in half an hour's time, so I think I'll probably need a walk with an alpaca after that, don't you? That should be a good way of putting the de-stressing theory to the test.'

'You're going to meet Cesare Montorso?' There was awe in Alfonso's voice. 'Are you sure that's a good idea? We saw that article in the paper at the weekend. I bet he's furious.'

'I imagine he is, but I think it's my duty to at least try to mediate.'

'Well, good luck with that, Alice. I think you'll need it.' There was renewed respect in his voice but, also, more than a touch of concern.

In consequence Alice was feeling quite nervous when she arrived at the *municipio* at twelve. She was greeted cordially enough by the man on the front desk who asked her to take a seat and wait. Less than a minute later a tall man in his sixties emerged from a side door and came across to where she was sitting. Even without seeing the photo in the paper she felt sure she would have recognised him, as the similarity between him and his sons was all too obvious. In spite of what she had heard about him, this gave her a strange feeling of familiarity. She stood up to shake hands.

'*Buongiorno, Signor Montorso.*'

He didn't return her smile, but he shook her hand politely enough and led her through to his office. This was a big room overlooking a well-tended ornamental garden which she hadn't realised existed at the rear of the building. He waved her into a seat and then sat down behind his desk which was groaning with paperwork. 'How can I help you, signora?'

Alice took a deep breath and launched into the speech she had been preparing. 'As I told your receptionist, my name is Alice Sterling and I'm the recently appointed manager of Varaldo Castle. I'm British, but I've lived in Italy for a number of years and my background is in estate management.' Having established her credentials, she went on to the matter in hand. 'As you know, the Varaldo family intend to open the castle to the public, and I've come to see you to explain how I believe this will have a positive effect on the town.'

As she ran through what she saw as the list of potential benefits ranging from employment opportunities to increased trade for local businesses, she kept a careful eye on his expression. It remained impassive, almost as though he wasn't even listening, and by the time she came to the end of her little speech, she had absolutely no idea what reaction to expect from him. To her surprise, it was affable – initially.

'Thank you for coming to see me, I appreciate the courtesy. Certainly it's more courtesy than I've ever received from any member of the Varaldo family. The fact is, however, that I don't accept the scenario you present. Far from improving the quality of life for the people of the town, I fear that such a step would be counterproductive and should be opposed.'

'And that's why you've called the referendum?'

'I believe it's only right and democratic for the local inhabitants to be able to vote on such a major issue.'

Alice was genuinely surprised at how reasonable he was sounding and she was even beginning to question whether everybody, including his sons, might be wrong about him when his attitude suddenly changed. In fact, it changed so quickly it was as if a switch had been flicked. One minute he was the smooth politician, the next he was something far more primal.

'This town doesn't belong to the Varaldo family to treat as their personal fiefdom. Those days have gone! We're not in the Middle Ages now!'

Alice could almost have smiled to hear him using the same language the baroness had used only a few hours earlier, but the rising anger she sensed in him and the bitter expression on his face wiped away any thought of smiling. There was no question that he looked and sounded intimidating, but she knew she had at least to try.

'Surely that's the whole point, Signor Montorso. We're living in the twenty-first century now and there's no place for family feuds. I've got to know the Varaldo family well since I started working here and I'm quite sure that none of them harbours any kind of old-fashioned sense of superiority or entitlement. They're just a country family trying to do what's best for the family... and the town.' Seeing him about to erupt, she ploughed on. 'What I came to say to you today was that the family weren't behind Saturday's newspaper article. Getting the *Gazzetta* involved was my idea, as a means of generating popular support in favour of the conversion of the castle into a tourist attraction. The Varaldo family specifically told me to avoid any mention of the historic conflict between their family and yours, and I respected that. The journalist sniffed out the story of the long-standing rivalry for himself.'

'I don't believe you. That sort of thing just reeks of Varaldo deceit. They're the scum of the earth!'

The mayor gave an angry snarl, and flecks of spit actually flew from his mouth onto the desk between them. Instinctively, Alice pulled back, but she remembered Fenella's words about dealing with bullies and persevered.

'Believe what you like, but I'm telling you the truth and I don't like being called a liar. The Varaldo family are good people and I'm proud to work for them.' She stood up and returned his belligerent stare. 'And it's my belief that the people of the town feel the same way as I do about the family. I came here today to have a calm, pragmatic conversation with you, not a slanging match. Good luck with your referendum, but I believe the result will come as a shock to you.' She could see him getting redder and redder in the face and so, before he either leapt over the desk and physically attacked her or burst a blood vessel, she headed for the door, stopping only to wish him good day before leaving.

As preparation for a stress-relieving walk with an alpaca, this had to be as good as it got.

Although she had had some time to calm down over lunch, she was still feeling decidedly uptight when she met Alfonso at the gate to the alpaca field.

'How did it go with the mayor?'

'Well, he didn't physically assault me, but it was the strangest thing; one minute he was sounding very rational and almost conciliatory, and the next he changed completely, and I thought for a moment he might be about to explode.'

Alfonso nodded sagely. 'That's what everybody says these days. Let's face it, he's never been an easy person to get on with, but over the last few years he's been getting worse and worse. It's the sudden mood swings, just like the one you've been describing, that are more noticeable now. I was talking to Giovanni the baker just the other day and he told me Cesare suddenly picked up a handful of cream pastries and threw them around the shop just because he had to wait in a queue to be served. That's not rational behaviour. He should get himself looked at properly by a doctor, but apparently he refuses even to entertain the idea. Valentino at the *municipio*, who's always been one of his friends, tried telling him that, and Cesare threw a glass of water in his face.' Alfonso shook his head sadly. 'It's proper medical help the man needs.'

At that moment Alice spotted Pietro in the field behind his father approaching with a handsome pure white alpaca on a rope halter. For such a giant of a man he was being very gentle and stroking the long neck of the animal softly. For its part, the alpaca looked completely relaxed and docile. Alfonso opened the gate and beckoned to Alice to go in. Pietro led the alpaca up to her and handed her the end of the rope lead.

'This is Bianca. We called her that because of the colour of her coat.'

Growing up on a farm, Alice had considerable experience with animals and, as a youngster, had often exhibited ponies, sheep and even the bull with her father at the County Show, so leading an animal was nothing new to her. What was new was this particular breed of animal. Bianca was probably the size of a Shetland pony or maybe a little taller. Her shoulders were roughly level with Alice's waist while her head was level with Alice's shoulder. The most endearing feature was the enigmatic smile on the animal's face, not dissimilar to Frank the Labrador when he was splashing about in the pool. Alice stretched out her free hand and stroked the rough coat.

'She was sheared just before we got her so she's not as cuddly as she will be in the winter.' Pietro was looking positively paternal and it occurred to Alice that he would probably be the perfect person to supervise this new venture. She gave him and the alpaca a smile in return.

'Ciao, Bianca, are you coming for a walk with me?'

Pietro replied on the alpaca's behalf. 'For today, I thought you might just like to stay in this area until you feel comfortable with her. After that, you can take her out and walk anywhere you like. She's not in the least bit aggressive and I'm sure you'll find it a calming experience.' He gave her a little smile. 'It works on me.'

'And I'm quite sure you need some of that after your meeting with the mayor this morning.' Alfonso came up behind his son and gave Alice a soft pat on the shoulder. 'Full marks for going to see him. That was brave of you.'

'I'm glad I did, but I'm really quite worried about him, about his health. It was scary how he switched in an instant from nice to nasty. I'm sure psychologists have a name for that kind of thing. You're right, he definitely needs professional help but I suppose until he acknowledges he has a problem and asks for help, there's nothing to be done.' She returned her attention to the alpaca who was standing peaceably alongside her. 'Come on, Bianca, let's go for a walk and see if some of that alpaca calm rubs off on me.'

Chapter 21

The rest of the week was uneventful and Alice was grateful for that. After her confrontation with the mayor she had been expecting the worst but as the days went by, she began to hope that they would reach the referendum the following week without further conflict. On Tuesday, Luca's friend came to look at the Mercedes and predicted that, fully restored, it was likely to make a substantial amount at auction. He also promised to send a detailed estimate of the cost of restoration, all of which Alice reported to Simonetta first and then to Luca that evening on the phone. It gave her a perfect excuse to call him and when she heard his voice she felt that same little thrill of attraction run through her.

'Ciao, Luca, I thought I'd give you a call and tell you how it went with the classic car man today.'

'Ciao, Alice, it's great to hear from you. I've been thinking about calling you just to hear your voice.'

This sounded good and Alice settled down happily to chat to him, and they ended up talking for almost half an hour. When she recounted her meeting with his father the previous day she heard him give a sigh.

'You're so right, he needs medical help. You can see it, I can see it, and Tommy can see it; everybody can, except my father. Sooner or later something bad is going to happen, and I just wish we could get in there and sort him out before he flips completely.'

When she finally wished him good night and put down the phone she felt a pang of separation. At least she had Sunday's trip to the Tuscan mountains to look forward to. There was no getting away from it: she was hooked on this man.

The visit by the antiques expert revealed a number of potentially valuable pieces – most notably a medieval tapestry probably worth in excess of a hundred thousand euros – but the baron was still adamant that he didn't want to sell until it became absolutely necessary. Interestingly, they received an estimate from Luca that same day indicating that, coincidently, he reckoned that the sale of the car should go a long way towards covering the first stage of the building works and modernization of the castle. To the chagrin of the antiques man, it was decided that none of the contents would be sold for now.

When Saturday afternoon came along, Alice was only too happy to go for a ride on Horace the horse. She had enjoyed her stroll through the fields with the alpaca on Monday a lot more than she had been expecting and had emerged at the end of it feeling more at peace, but she knew that her first love would always be horses. As Luca was away, Simonetta joined her and they followed the usual route up the hill above the mayor's farm, but this time without seeing any members of his family. Alice queried when Simonetta would next get a chance to meet up with Tommi and saw her friend shake her head ruefully.

'I haven't seen him all week and it looks as though I won't see him until after this damn referendum next

Friday. Apparently his father's been in his office at the town hall all day every day making calls and sending messages to everybody from the President of the Republic to the Pope. The farmhand they've had for years finally left last week after being shouted at by Cesare once too often. In consequence, Tommi's had sole responsibility for the farm and he's been getting up before dawn and not getting back into the house again until after dark. I do feel so very sorry for him.'

Alice reflected that the repercussions of the mayor's eccentric behaviour were causing real hardship to so many, and she wondered if the farmhand would find it easy to get another job. A thought occurred to her. 'The farmhand, was he good at his job?'

'Very, apparently. Tommi says he's been there for years and years and he knows the workings of the farm inside out. It'll be hard to replace him.'

'Might it be an idea for *us* to employ him? We could definitely do with another pair of hands alongside Alfonso and his son. The new tractor and modern machinery will be arriving in the next week or two, and the first job will be to start preparing a couple of fields for winter feed. Alfonso says we should also grow maize for the chickens, rather than rely on always buying stuff in.'

'That sounds like a good idea.' Simonetta glanced across at Alice and grinned. 'But I'm not sure that Tommi's father will feel the same way about it if we do employ his man.'

'Why don't you get his number from Tommi and give him a call? Or I will, if you like. The way things are at the moment, it's probably not that easy for him to find a new job, so we'd be doing him a favour.'

'I'll do that. You're right, the poor man might be desperate.'

This time they rode right up almost to the top of the ridge and stopped to give the horses a rest on the open grassland. As they sat looking back down over the valley, Simonetta brought up the subject of Luca. 'Tommi's been talking to Luca who told him the two of you are going out for the day tomorrow. Does that mean things are getting serious between you two?'

Alice answered honestly. 'I really hope so. The thing is, he seems to be taking it very slowly. I mean, it's nice that he's not just assuming I'd be ready to jump into bed with him after only a first date, but I get the feeling something might be holding him back.' She glanced across at her friend and voiced her overarching fear. 'I was wondering if he's found out that I'm disabled and he's chosen to just be friends because of that.'

Simonetta snorted. 'Don't be so silly. He's better than that. If he likes you, he'll like you no matter what.'

'That's what I'm hoping, but deep down I'm scared stiff. Mind you, here I am saying that he's taking *his* time, but I still haven't found the courage to tell him about my leg in case it frightens him off. So far everything's been going so perfectly and I don't want to ruin it.'

'And I'm sure it'll continue to go perfectly. When are you going to tell him?'

'Tomorrow, when we're in the mountains.'

'Good. That way you'll see that I'm right. Try not to worry about it. What I can tell you is that you're just about the first woman he's been out with for ages. Tommi says he's been buried in his work, so the fact that he's started asking you out means he's serious. He's probably just taking it slow so he doesn't frighten *you* off.' She gave Alice a smile. 'And, to me, it sounds as though he really likes you.'

'I wonder.'

When Alice saw Luca at the door next morning, she instinctively opened her arms to him and kissed him on the cheeks, loving the contact. For his part, he looked equally pleased to see her, as was his canine best buddy who stood on his hind legs, scrabbling at her with his paws. Wisely she had swapped her white jeans for blue jeans today.

'Hi, Alice. Frank, get down and leave the lady alone.'

'It's great to see you both. It's lovely weather, isn't it?' She groaned internally. The weather. Surely she could have thought of something a bit more meaningful to say? Still, he nodded back at her and led her and the dog to the car. It was a warm, sunny day and the roof was down, so Luca settled Frank in the back and tied his lead to the door pillar just in case he should take it into his head to think about jumping out of the moving vehicle.

As they drove west towards the mountains, with Luca occasionally reminding the dog that he was not supposed to slobber all over their hair or nibble their ears, they chatted easily and Alice felt ever more comfortable in his company – all except for nerves at the thought of his potential reaction to the revelation she was going to give him about her leg. They headed upwards via a never-ending series of bends into the higher mountains, soon driving through woods and picturesque villages into the increasingly remote heart of the Apennines. With the roof down, the sun shining, and a most appealing man at her side, Alice reflected that she hadn't been this happy for months, maybe years.

But would she still be feeling happy on the way back?

Luca pointed out their destination long before they reached it. 'Up there on the hilltop. It's an old tower built in the twelve hundreds, but it's been almost totally neglected for centuries and it needed a lot of structural work done on it. It used to belong to the all-powerful Medici family back in Renaissance times.'

Alice followed his pointing finger and could just make out the tower amid the trees on the top of a big hill in the distance – in Britain it would have been called a mountain. 'Wow, that's a long way up.'

'Don't worry, we can get right up to it in the car, although the last bit's very rough. I'm afraid the Porsche isn't really the right sort of car for my line of work but I love it dearly. There's no space in the boot for all my paraphernalia, there's barely enough room for Frank, and it doesn't like potholes, but I love it all the same and I owe it to Mario to hang on to it. If you don't mind a bit of exercise, we can leave the car where the proper road finishes and walk up the track. That way Frank will be able to run off a bit of his excess energy.'

They abandoned the car in a tiny hamlet beyond which the road turned into a farm track which was easy to walk on but clearly not designed for a low-slung sports car. Fortunately by this time they weren't too far from the top of the hill but, even so, it took them almost half an hour to get up to the tower and Alice could feel herself starting to limp by the time they got there. The temperature up here in the mountains was lower than back in Varaldo, but she was sweating all the same by the time they finished their climb. The views were stunning in all directions and the ancient tower itself was mightily impressive.

It was a perfectly round structure, perched on top of a rocky outcrop. Although the cliffs around it weren't quite vertical, the slopes were steep enough to have Alice worrying in case Frank decided to chase a rabbit over the edge, but he seemed quite happy to stick by the two of them and Luca told her he'd been up here before many times without incident. The rough hillside was covered in dense forest, some of the trees clearly many years old, and the terrain was anything but hospitable. Directly behind them stood an even more imposing mountain, Emilia-Romagna's highest point, Monte Cimone. This was a remote area and the tower looked impregnable, as indeed it was. Luca confirmed that, like Varaldo Castle, it had never been taken by an opposing force and Alice could well believe it. Trying to get an army up here would have been fraught with difficulty.

Luca left Frank with her while he went off to check that everything was as it should be in readiness for tomorrow's inspection. Gratefully, Alice sat down on a boulder and stretched her legs as she prepared herself for the confession that was to come. She stared at the old stones, wondering what it must have been like to spend a winter up here in what would have been very Spartan conditions. At her feet, Frank – who seemed unconcerned that his master had gone off and left him – took advantage of the pause to sprawl on the grassy slope, panting after his exertions. All around were more tree-clad hills and there was little or no sign of human habitation apart from a couple of distant ski lifts and the roofs of Tuscany's best-known ski resort of Abetone. She was still doing her best to concentrate on the view, rather than what was to come, when she heard footsteps behind her and felt Luca's hand touch her shoulder as he squatted down beside her.

'Look up there.'

Remembering how she had misinterpreted his intentions last Sunday night, she resisted the temptation to grab hold of him and kiss him; instead she obediently followed the direction of his pointing finger. Almost immediately she saw what had attracted his attention. There were two huge birds wheeling in the clear blue sky. He kept his voice low, even though the birds themselves were probably a hundred metres above them, maybe more.

'Can you see them? They're eagles. They're very rare here. We're lucky to see them.'

She sat there and looked up in awe as the majestic birds scoured the hillsides for some poor unsuspecting little animal to provide them with lunch. She liked the feel of Luca's hand on her shoulder and she leant against him, feeling his warmth through her arm. Then, all too soon, he removed his hand and suggested that they should follow the example of the eagles.

'Feel like lunch?'

The way she was feeling up here with him in this romantic spot, food wasn't high on her agenda, but she nodded all the same.

'Sounds good. Is everything ready for the inspectors?'

'It should be fine. I know the builders quite well by now and they've done a good job. I'd like to ask them for a quotation for Varaldo Castle if you agree. They're real specialists in old properties.'

'Definitely, particularly as you've worked with them before. It's a beautiful spot up here, isn't it?'

'Absolutely, although it's a fortress, it somehow feels very peaceful. It makes a real change from the cares of everyday life.'

Thought of the cares of everyday life finally galvanised her into action. She couldn't put it off any longer. 'Luca, would you mind sitting down for a moment? There's something I need to tell you.' She could hear the tension in her voice and he must have picked up on it.

'Of course, is something wrong? Are you all right?' There was real concern in his voice and she took heart from it.

He sat down on the boulder alongside her and she launched into her prepared speech, choosing her words carefully. 'I need to tell you what happened to me. You see, four years ago I was caught in an avalanche high up in the Dolomites.' She shot him a glance and saw him watching her attentively. 'I was trapped for almost an hour until I was found by a rescue dog.' The stress of the memory must have infused her voice and attracted Frank's attention as there was a movement at her feet and the Labrador's head landed softly on her lap. Clearly, he had been listening and had picked up on the emotion in her voice.

'Were you hurt?' Luca's voice was low.

'My shin and ankle were caught between two rocks and severely crushed.' She took a deep breath as the memory of the agonising pain returned. 'As a result, my left leg had to be amputated below the knee.' To make sure there could be no confusion in his mind, she lifted her hand from caressing the dog's ears and tapped her prosthetic limb, producing a dull clunk. 'So that means I'm now legally disabled. I have a stick – even if I try not to use it too often – and I know I'll never run or dance again.' It was a struggle to keep her voice level.

His hand instantly reached over and caught hold of hers, and she felt him give it a squeeze.

'Running and dancing are seriously overrated pastimes.' He gave her a little smile, raised her hand to his mouth and kissed her fingers one by one. 'You can walk, you can ride, you can drive a car, you can hold down a big job and you do all that while still managing to look gorgeous. You're an inspiration.'

She felt such an intense wave of relief wash over her that she couldn't help herself. She burst into tears. His arm encircled her shoulders and pulled her tightly against him. As she sobbed into his chest, she was dimly aware of a cold wet nose poking her ear and she heard Luca remonstrating with Frank to get off. The banality of this helped immensely and she straightened up, reaching into the pocket of her jeans for a tissue. She wiped her eyes and blinked a few times as she looked up at him.

'You don't mind?'

'Do I mind? Of course I do!' There was real strength in his voice now. 'Do I mind that you almost got killed? Yes, I do, because if that had happened, I would never have met you. Do I mind that you felt you had to confess this to me as if I might object? Yes, I do. In case you hadn't noticed, Alice Sterling, I like you a lot and I like all of you, from your blue-grey eyes to the brain in there behind them and the rest of you – and that includes your legs, your arms and all the other bits, whether you've had them all your life or whether they've been added later. What I mind most of all, though, is the fact that you thought I might somehow think less of you as a result of something like that. So, in answer to your question, yes, of course I damn well mind.'

In case there might be any lingering doubt in her mind, he pulled her close once more and kissed her tenderly on the lips. As he did so, she felt as if her heart might explode with joy. Apart from delight at his reaction to her tale, the all-encompassing feeling running through her was one of relief; relief that she had finally managed to unburden herself of the weight of the secret she had been keeping, not just from him, but from so many people. Somehow this simple admission to him had lifted some of the enormous grey cloud that had been hanging over her for four long years. All right, she had a prosthetic leg, but so what? It was nothing to feel guilty about. She felt relieved, but also liberated, like she was finally emerging from a deep dark chasm into the daylight.

Lunch was in a tiny restaurant – hardly more than a bar with a few tables – at the side of a minor road in a little hamlet, partway down a series of hairpin bends on the other side of Abetone. A plaque on the wall indicated their altitude as 1200 metres above sea level, and the air was cooler but not cold as they sat outside under a faded Martini umbrella. From here they had a breath-taking view down over the foothills of the Apennines into Tuscany to the south. The road signs were already pointing towards Florence, and Alice knew she would have to take a trip down to visit the city sometime soon. Luca's Medici tower was just discernible in the distance behind them and there was hardly a sound to be heard. As she sat back and relaxed, her feet serving as a headrest for the weary dog beneath the table, she smiled across at Luca.

'What a wonderful place. Thanks for bringing me here.'

He smiled back at her. 'I'm very glad you could come. I've been here two or three times now, but this is the first time I've brought someone with me.'

She caught his eye for a moment. 'Do you really live such a solitary existence? Surely you must have loads of friends.'

'Of course I have friends, but I suppose it's true that I have been a bit of a hermit over the past few years. Mainly it's because I've been concentrating on building up the business.'

She took a chance. 'And the other part?'

Luca's gaze drifted to the landscape beyond them. 'Let's just say that things have been complicated for me on the personal front over the past few years.' He suddenly looked right at her. 'You've no idea how great it is to be here like this with you. Thank you so much.'

To Alice's annoyance just then the owner arrived with a verbal menu and on Luca's recommendation she chose cold smoked fillets of trout from a nearby river and a mixed salad that arrived loaded with everything from artichoke hearts to quails' eggs and walnuts from the surrounding trees. Accompanied by a glass of cold rosé, it was delicious. As they ate, they continued to chat and she could feel Luca relaxing more and more in her company and she in his. She would very much have liked to ask him more about the complications to his personal life he had mentioned, but she could tell he preferred to steer clear of these, at least for now.

In the afternoon they drove lazily back through the hills towards home, stopping from time to time to give

Frank a walk and to stretch their legs. Around four o'clock they reached a tiny village with, amazingly, a gelateria boasting a mouth-watering selection of home-made ice cream. Needless to say, Luca had refused her offer to pay for lunch, but this time she put her foot down and insisted the least she could do was to buy him an ice cream now and give him a cup of tea when they got home. It was a lovely afternoon but he didn't return to talking about anything too personal and she thought it best to give him time and space, although her instincts were increasingly to throw herself into his arms. The more she got to know this kind, generous, handsome man, the more she realised she really did like him a lot – maybe more than like.

They finally returned to Varaldo and as agreed he came in for a cup of tea and a slice of the cake she had made the previous day. This was a lemon drizzle cake and, although she reckoned she should have added a bit more lemon, it tasted okay and he sounded enthusiastic. He then surprised her.

'This cake is so much better than the ones I produce.' He grinned. 'I blame it on the old oven in my place.'

'You bake your own cakes?' Was she hearing right? This was surely the Holy Grail of boyfriends – although, she was quick to remind herself that he wasn't her boyfriend yet. But a man who could bake? 'Wow, I'm impressed.'

He was still grinning. 'When I was working for Mario – he's a baker and he specialises in the finest pastries and cakes – I learnt to make all sorts of stuff from profiteroles to rye bread.'

Barely half an hour later he reluctantly stood up and told her he had to go. Overcome with the desire to continue their time together, she stood up too and grasped tightly him around the waist, pressing herself against him.

'Are you sure you wouldn't like to stay? I wish you would.' And she wasn't just talking about staying for more tea.

She felt his lips press against her forehead. 'There's nothing I'd like more, but I have to be in Rome for a meeting at ten o'clock tomorrow morning so I need to get back to Parma to catch the train this evening. I'm staying with friends in Rome and they haven't met Frank yet and they've told me to bring him. This'll be the first time he's ever been on a train so wish me luck – it could be chaos. I'll be home late on Tuesday night so how about you come to my place on Wednesday or Thursday and I'll cook for you? Would you like that?'

'I'd love that.'

She kissed him with real passion and knew that time would pass all too slowly before they were together again. Still, she told herself pragmatically, at least she now had something to look forward to, and it was looking as though her fears had come to nothing. Finally, regretfully, he tore himself away and she could still feel his touch as she watched his car disappear down the road.

Chapter 22

Next morning's family meeting produced an interesting development. Once everybody was seated, the baron held up a formal-looking white envelope and brandished it at them. 'This arrived in the post for me this morning. I'll read it to you.'

As the others sat back and listened, he read out the letter. It was from the mayor's office at the town hall informing the baron that there would be a public meeting at six o'clock on Wednesday evening to discuss the plans to develop the castle into a tourist attraction. Members of the family and/or their representatives were invited to attend. When the baron reached the end of the letter he looked around the room. In case the full ramifications of this had not registered with everybody, he proceeded to spell them out.

'Under normal circumstances in a situation like this I would expect the architect in charge of the project to be there. I imagine the mayor will have assembled a number of so-called experts to try to prove that we shouldn't go ahead with our plans, and it really needs a qualified and experienced person to reply to any technical questions, not just us as the owners of the property. The problem, of course, is that the architect in question happens to be the mayor's son and the two haven't spoken for years.'

Alice and Simonetta exchanged glances but it was the elderly baroness who spoke up.

'You're totally right, Lodovico, the architect must be there, but he probably knew that this day would come and I'm sure he can handle it. I do think either you or one of the children must be there as well. And Alice, of course.'

The baron looked determined. 'I most certainly will be there. I have no intention of letting Cesare Montorso claim that I'm deliberately staying away. I know the man; if I don't go, he'll say that I have no concern for the local people and consider myself far too high and mighty to get involved with the common man. Well, I intend to be there to prove him wrong.' He let his eyes sweep across the room again. 'Naturally if Alice would like to come, and if either or both of you children would like to come, I'll be more than happy, but this is something I've got to do, and I agree with you, mother, we will need the architect by our sides.'

Alice was delighted to hear the steely resolve in his voice. With his rather woolly, absent-minded manner, she had somehow been expecting him to delegate responsibility elsewhere, and she was pleased to find him prepared to step up to the mark. An image of him dressed in one of the suits of armour from the corridor crossed her mind and she smiled to herself. Clearly, if the mayor was looking for a fight, the baron was up for it. As for Luca, she felt sure that this meeting would prove far more stressful than a normal public meeting because of the presence of his father, but as the baroness had said, he must have known when he took the job that at some point a confrontation would have been likely. Simonetta's voice interrupted her thoughts.

'Good for you, Papà.' She sounded genuinely proud. 'I'm definitely going to be there. Achille, what about you? Can you make it on Wednesday evening?'

'Of course. I have a meeting in Parma that afternoon, but I'll make sure to be back in time. I agree with you completely: we need to show a united front.'

Simonetta transferred her attention to Alice. 'And of course you must be there, Alice. Would you be kind enough to call Luca and tell him about this, please? I'm afraid it'll come as unwelcome news to him.'

News of the meeting certainly didn't come as welcome news to Luca when she called him on his mobile, but from his voice it sounded as if it wasn't that much of a surprise. 'I was wondering if he might do something like this. In fact, I'm impressed that he's actually behaving like a proper public official and including the populace in the decision-making process – or at least trying to give that impression. With the referendum coming up, a public meeting makes a lot of sense.'

'And how do you feel about being there? It'll mean seeing and probably talking to your father again.'

'I've known from the start that this was going to be almost inevitable. To be quite honest, although part of me is dreading it, deep down inside I'd like to see the man again, even if it's just to discover if he's really become as bad as people say. As for possible objections, I've been preparing some ammunition, so I should be able to field any awkward questions.'

Wednesday's meeting took place in a large room in the town's Community Centre and when Alice walked in with the family she was mildly surprised to see that almost all the seats were already taken. Whether this was because the mayor had made sure that all his supporters were in attendance or whether this indicated genuine interest on the part of the population of Varaldo remained to be seen. Seats in the front row had been kept for the family so Alice and the others had to walk down the central aisle to take their places. Simonetta offered to take her grandmother's arm, but the proud old lady shrugged off the offer and managed it all by herself. Alice and Luca walked side-by-side and she was pleased to see him being greeted by a good number of people as he made his way through the crowd. Among these were Giorgio from the restaurant, Alice's landlords, and Emilia from the stables. There was no sign of Luca's twin brother, but this was no doubt because he was back home looking after the farm single-handed.

Alice sat down next to Luca and, in spite of the circumstances, a little tingle of pleasure ran through her as she felt his warmth beside her. In front of them, a table had been set up on one side of the stage with a dais on the other. Behind the desk was the town clerk and another staff member from the *municipio*. A few minutes after six the mayor appeared on stage and made his way over to the dais and waited while the town clerk called for silence. Alice kept a careful eye on Cesare Montorso. Tonight he was looking smart, business-like and even affable, smiling and waving to faces he recognised in the audience. If he noticed his son in the front row, he gave no sign of acknowledgement. When he started to speak, he produced a brief outline of his main objections to any development of the castle and then called two expert witnesses: one from the university of Bologna and one from something called the Italian Rural Life Society. Simonetta whispered in Alice's ear that she had never heard of this group, and Alice turned towards Luca on the other side of her to check with him but when she saw the concentration on his face she decided not to bother him with questions.

She could see that his attention was totally focused on his father. She could only imagine what must be going through his head after over fifteen years apart. The fact that his father was looking presentable and sounding professional probably came as a surprise after the horror stories circulating in the village, and Alice wondered whether Luca might be having second thoughts about his decision to support his father's sworn enemies.

The white-haired professor from the university of Bologna launched into a long rambling discourse about medieval castle building without really making any particular point relevant to this meeting. The man from the so-called Rural Life Society did his best to convince the audience that the town would instantly be inundated with floods of tourists and that this would completely change the character of the place as traffic chaos ensued. It was quite clear that he was one of those people who were not prepared to accept change of any kind and Alice wondered how many people in the audience would in fact sympathise with this view. When he finally sat down again, the Town Clerk turned towards the baron and asked if he or his representative had anything to say.

As already agreed, the baron deferred to his architect and Luca stood up and climbed the half dozen steps onto the stage. As he passed in front of his father, he gave him a formal nod and Alice clearly heard him say, 'Good evening, Mr Mayor.' The mayor gave no sign of even hearing this and his face remained impassive as Luca walked up to the dais and looked out over the audience.

'Good evening, ladies and gentlemen. My name is Luca Montorso and I'm the architect responsible for the project to open Varaldo Castle to the public. For those of you who don't know, the mayor is my father, and it grieves me that he has chosen to let his personal animosity towards me and the Varaldo family stand in the way of what will be without question a blessing to the town. The castle is almost a thousand years old and has a unique place in Italian history. It deserves to be opened to people from all over the country and, indeed, the world, to visit and explore. Up till now, few of us have ever seen inside the castle, and I salute Baron Lodovico for his decision to share his home with the world.'

He went on to list the advantages he believed this would bring to the town and followed this with a well-reasoned demolition of the objections of the two 'expert' witnesses. By the end, Alice sensed that many in the audience had been swayed by his words and for the first time she saw an expression of frustration or more on the face of the mayor. After Luca had finished speaking, there was a round of applause and the face of the mayor darkened even further. As his son left the stage, he leapt to his feet and strode across to the dais. Alice saw concern on the face of the town clerk who looked as though he was trying to catch the mayor's eye to dissuade him from doing anything silly, but Cesare Montorso was beyond listening to reason. He stared malignantly down at his son with a look of such bitter hatred in his eyes that it actually drew a gasp from members of the audience.

'Traitor! How can you betray generations of your fore-fathers by working for scum like the Varaldo family? They deserve to be wiped off the face of the earth.' He stabbed a finger towards Luca. 'And you with them!'

By now he was screaming at the top of his voice, oblivious to the remonstrations of the town clerk who repeatedly beat his gavel on the desk in front of him, but in vain. Alice even saw the clerk eyeing the security guard at the side of the stage when the mayor suddenly rattled off a string of foul expletives directed at the Varaldo family and his son, turned and stormed off the stage. There was stunned silence in the hall for several seconds after this outburst before a hum of conversation started. Alice turned to Luca who had returned to his seat beside her and laid a hand on his arm.

'He's not well, Luca. He needs help.'

'He certainly does.' There was a mixture of shock and pity in his voice. After a few seconds' pause, he stood up and glanced down at her. 'This won't take long.'

She saw him climb up onto the stage and have a few words with the town clerk who listened intently before giving a sign of agreement. As he banged his gavel for silence, Luca walked back across to the dais and waited for almost half a minute before the audience quietened down.

'Ladies and gentlemen, I feel I must apologise for my father's behaviour. He's not a well man or he wouldn't have used the language that he did. On behalf of the Montorso family, I'm truly sorry.'

With a nod to the town clerk he came back down the steps again as everybody started leaving the hall. Alice and the Varaldo family also stood up, waiting their turn to file out. As they did so, a number of people came past to offer their verbal support, and it was increasingly clear that the mayor had shot himself squarely in the foot.

The baron insisted on taking the family out for dinner at the Casa Rosa along with Alice and Luca. They all sat down around a large table and started chatting sporadically. It was hard to gauge how they were all feeling. On the one hand, Alice was sure that they had all sensed the mood in the hall swing in favour of their application, but at the same time, there was no doubt that all of them had been stunned by the mayor's incredible outburst. The fact that this violent reaction had almost certainly had an adverse effect on his cause and might even lead to his political downfall would definitely help *their* cause, but it was tragic in its own way, particularly for Luca and his brother. In spite of everything, she almost felt pity for the mayor. Pity, however, was not something that the restaurateur was feeling. He arrived at their table looking decidedly buoyant.

'Well done, Luca. I'm sure the public will share your view that opening the castle to the public will be a very positive step for everybody. I don't think your father did himself any favours tonight, and I'm sure that'll help sway any floating voters. Now what can I get you to eat? Leonardo has had me working all afternoon making fresh pasta. How about a salad with ham and parmesan followed by a plate of *tagliatelle noci e gorgonzola*? The sauce is made with walnuts from our own tree.'

They were happy to agree with his suggestions and he went off to fetch wine and water for them. He returned almost immediately with slightly sparkling white wine and a rich red wine and saw that everybody was served before leaving them to it. The baron raised his glass towards Luca and proposed a toast.

'*Architetto* Montorso... Luca, that was an excellent speech. Thank you most warmly. Cheers.' They all took sips of wine before the baron carried on, this time in more sober tones. 'I'm afraid I was appalled by your father's behaviour, but I confess to feeling almost sorry for the man. He obviously needs help. Maybe tonight's outburst will push some of his close friends into persuading him to seek medical help. It's tragic, really.'

Alice was interested to see that the baron's reaction had been similar to her own. The mayor totally losing it on stage hadn't been a pretty sight and she could imagine the conflicting emotions running through Luca now. He was sitting to the right of her with the baroness on the other side of him and they were deep in conversation. Achille was sitting on the other side of Alice so she started to chat to the man who would one day inherit the baronetcy. She remembered the conversation she had had with Silvia, the lovesick housemaid, and decided that this was as good a time as any to approach Achille about it. She waited until most of the others were chatting animatedly before turning towards him, lowering her voice before bringing the subject up as tentatively as possible.

'I had a chat to Silvia a little while ago. She's nice, isn't she?'

His cheeks immediately blushed red and he glanced furtively up the table towards his father who was still fully involved in conversation with Lady Beatrice. 'Silvia's lovely...' His voice tailed off poignantly and she tried again.

'It's nothing to do with me, so do tell me to mind my own business, but I get the feeling there's a real spark between you two.' Alice caught his eye for a second before he dropped his gaze to his glass. 'Or am I mistaken?'

She had to wait a few seconds for his answer, delivered in a whisper. 'You aren't wrong – at least as far as I'm concerned. I think the world of her.'

'Well, if you want my opinion I feel sure she feels the same way about you.'

'You really think she does?' He looked up at her eagerly, an expression of joyful hope on his face. 'Honestly?'

'Honestly. I'm sure.' She didn't tell him that it had been Silvia herself who had given her this idea. 'Does this mean you haven't told her how you feel?'

He shook his head. 'I've been wanting to, but I've never had the courage to say anything. What if she were to tell me she didn't feel the same way or, even worse, what if she were to be so outraged that she decided to go off and leave. I couldn't bear that.'

Alice struggled not to smile. Here he was, the future Baron Varaldo and he sounded more like an insecure teenager.

'Well, if you want my advice – and like I said it's no business of mine so just ignore what I have to say if you wish – but I think it's time the two of you sat down and had a talk.' A thought occurred to her, not for the first time. 'What do you think your father's reaction would be if you told him you were in love with Silvia?'

'That's the other thing. I've been asking myself that for ages now. I must admit I've been afraid he would disapprove, but since you and Simonetta have been able to persuade him to accept Luca as one of us, and to accept Tommaso as Simonetta's boyfriend, I've been coming round to thinking that maybe Papà's not so set in his ways after all. Do you really think I should speak to her?'

'I most certainly do.'

During the excellent meal, Alice gradually managed to get Luca to start talking, and by the end he was sounding more like his normal self again. When the party broke up, she stood with him outside the restaurant while the others climbed into Achille's car and set off back to the castle. As they disappeared from sight, she reached over and caught hold of his hand.

'Feeling better?'

He turned towards her and she saw a smile on his face in the orange glow of the street light. 'I'm fine, thanks. Having you beside me was a great help.' And, to her delight, he leant down and kissed her softly on the lips. 'Definitely a great help.' Then, to her acute disappointment, he pointed across the road to where his car was parked. 'I'm afraid I have to get back to Parma now. I'm desperately trying to get some plans drawn up for the City Council and there's going to be a meeting tomorrow, so I'm afraid I'll be burning the midnight oil.'

'That's a real shame. I was going to ask if you wanted coffee at my place.'

'And I would have said yes like a shot. Anyway, can we still have dinner tomorrow?' He stopped and corrected himself. 'Sorry, tomorrow's no good. I've got another appointment, but let's make it Friday. I promise. Okay?'

'I can't wait.' She kissed him in return and felt a thrill as he responded, but all too soon he stepped back and shot her a regretful glance.

'See you on Friday.'

Chapter 23

The referendum took place on Friday morning and the results were posted on the town website at three o'clock. Alice was at home, trying to make up her mind what to wear for dinner – or more – at Luca's house that night, and all the while she had been keeping an eye on her computer, waiting for the result to be announced. She was delighted to see that almost eighty percent of the voters had disagreed with the mayor and had supported the Varaldo family's efforts to go ahead with opening the castle to the public. The first person she called was Simonetta to check that she and the family had seen the result. Needless to say, they were all pleased and relieved. The next call was going to be to Luca to give him the good news but no sooner had she finished speaking to Simonetta than her phone started ringing. It was none other than Luca and she was quick to pass on the result of the vote. When he replied he sounded pleased but distracted.

'Look, I'm really, really sorry, but I'm going to have to cancel our dinner tonight. Something unexpected has come up and I have to go away for a few days.'

Doing her best to suppress a wave of disappointment, Alice pressed him for a bit more information and discovered that he was on his way to a place on the coast over a hundred kilometres below Rome, and that was a long way from Parma.

'I'll need the car when I'm down there so I'm going to have to drive. It's a horrible journey and it'll take me five or six hours – if I'm lucky. I can't take Frank with me this time so as soon as I've dropped him off with Carlo at the studio, I'll carry straight on. I'm really sorry about tonight but I have to go. I have no choice.' She heard him hesitate. 'It's… somebody I know down there. I'll tell you all about it when I get back. She's in hospital and I need to see her. I'm really, really sorry about tonight.'

Alice's mind was racing. He had told her that he had lived and worked south of Rome for some years after qualifying. It didn't take much to put two and two together. Maybe the woman in question was an old girlfriend – or not such an old one. Who was this mystery woman? Alice didn't have a chance to ask him any more as it was clear from his tone that he was in a mad hurry. A sudden thought occurred to her.

'What about Frank? You can't just leave him in the studio for days. Who's going to look after him?'

'Carlo says he'll take him. It's very good of him, considering he only lives in a very small flat, but hopefully I'll only be away for a couple of days.'

Alice made a quick decision. 'I can take Frank. I've got bags of room at my place, and if you aren't back by Monday I can take him into work with me. Besides, if I'm not going to see you, I can at least enjoy his company. I'm not working this afternoon so why don't you tell Carlo that I'll come and collect him from the studio in an hour or so? Would that help?'

Luca sounded only too happy to accept her offer and he thanked her profusely before ringing off, leaving her seriously puzzled. It was an uncomfortable feeling to find that she was being abandoned – at least temporarily – in favour of another woman, and the fact that he had never spoken about this woman made her feel even more uncomfortable. Who was she? This had to be more than a casual acquaintance as he was dropping everything and heading off on a long drive to see her. Maybe she was just a very close friend or might he have feelings for this woman? And, if so, where did this leave her?

She was still mulling it over as she drove down to Parma, squeezed the car into a tight parking space and took the lift up to Luca's studio. Here she found Carlo with Frank, and the Labrador gave her an enthusiastic welcome. As she collected his bed and a big bag of dry dog food she asked Carlo what he knew about the sudden departure of his boss, but he shook his head.

'I've no idea. He just called me and asked if I could take Frank.'

Alice did her best to sound blasé. 'Maybe he has a girlfriend down there.'

Carlo shrugged. 'If he has, it's the first I've heard of it. He goes to Rome and beyond on a pretty regular basis but he told me that's because he used to work down there. I've been working for him for three years and he's never mentioned another woman.'

Alice looked up from the dog in surprise. '*Another* woman?'

He grinned at her. 'Apart from you, of course. You're all he's been talking about for weeks – except for work.'

Alice had no idea how to reply to this, but it felt good.

When she got back home, she unloaded Frank's food and his bed in her flat and went up the stairs to check with Luisella that they didn't mind her having a canine guest for a few days. There was a brief standoff as Geronimo the terrier impressed on Frank that it was he who ruled this particular roost, and Frank, in spite of being three times his size, meekly acquiesced. Luisella assured Alice that Frank could stay as long as necessary and Alice decided to take him for a long walk, partly for his sake and partly to take her mind off her disappointment.

It was an overcast evening with rain in the air, which rather matched her mood. A few hours ago she had been happily looking forward to an evening and maybe a night with Luca, and now she was all on her own – apart from a big black dog. She walked up past the castle onto the track across Varaldo land that led upwards through the trees. Frank trotted along at her side and made occasional forays into the woods to bark at squirrels or to bring her sticks that she threw back into the trees for him to retrieve. He seemed quite unbothered by the absence of his master. The same couldn't be said for Alice.

When she emerged from the trees onto the open pastures, she sat down for a rest on a small rocky outcrop. She looked back down over the castle towards the mayor's farm on the other side of the valley where a red tractor was driving across the field where she had first set eyes on Tommaso that time with Simonetta. She was struck, as always, by how steep the slopes were and how unbelievable it appeared that a tractor could actually get up and down to plough the earth. She spared a thought for how tough life must have been for farm workers before the days of tractors and mechanical ploughs. Things had certainly been hard way back then and she was glad times had moved on.

As she sat there, she did her best to dismiss any further conjecture about Luca and this other woman and tried to concentrate instead on how well she had fitted in here in the Apennines and how happy she was – or had been up until a few hours ago. She felt completely comfortable with the Varaldo family now and had little doubt that she intended to stay here and make a permanent life for herself in Italy. Hopefully now that the referendum had proved overwhelmingly that there was support in the town for the development, things would be able to move ahead quickly. Her fear that the baron would be refused permission to open the castle to the public and thus do her out of a job looked less likely, and as Luca had said, by next Easter it should be up and running and she would be even busier.

Hopefully she and Luca would get together long before then, but if not, she told herself sternly, she was still going to make sure she kept on enjoying herself. This place and this job added up to a meaningful and satisfying life with or without the presence of this appealing, but enigmatic, man – or, indeed, any man. She talked it over with the dog who listened intently but didn't look convinced that she could do without his master. But then, neither was she.

She was just thinking about getting up to continue her walk when she heard a shout. Looking down the slope, she saw two figures emerge from the trees and she felt a smile spread across her face at the realisation that these were Achille and Silvia out for a walk together, hand in hand. They came up to where she was sitting and sat down alongside her, both with dreamy expressions on their faces in spite of the drizzly conditions. While Achille made a fuss of Frank, he explained that today he had followed Alice's advice and finally bitten the bullet and told Silvia how he felt about her. Alice didn't need to be told that Silvia's reaction had been ecstatic. Alice beamed at them, delighted at their obvious happiness, while doing her best to stifle any feeling of envy.

'I'm so glad you finally told each other how you feel. What about the next step? When are you going to tell the baron?'

Silvia and Achille exchanged glances and he nodded. 'Now… or at least when we get back from this walk. It's time we told him, told everybody.'

'Good for you. I'm sure he'll be only too happy for you. After all, he's accepted Tommaso and Simonetta as a couple and Luca as a member of the team. He's proved that he's a thoroughly modern man, not stuck in the past. He'll be delighted.'

The happy couple cuddled up against each other, their happiness only too visible. Then Silvia came up with an observation that proved she didn't miss much.

'What's the matter, Alice? You don't look your usual cheerful self.'

For a moment, Alice almost blurted out her fears that Luca might have another woman, but she decided to keep this to herself until she knew more. Instead, she just smiled back and shook her head ruefully. 'I was supposed to be going out for dinner tonight with Luca but he's been called away.' Doing her best to sound positive, she pointed down to where the Labrador was rolling happily about in the damp grass at their feet. 'Still, he's left me the next best thing.' As the first drops of serious rain began to fall, she stood up. 'Come on, Frank, let's try and get home before we get completely soaked. Besides, knowing you, I imagine you're ready for something to eat.'

She left the happy couple who seemed oblivious to the rain and made her way back down the hill. She was soaked by the time she got home and had to change into dry clothes. After doing her best to dry the soaking wet dog with an old towel, she poured dog food into his bowl and marvelled at the speed with which he devoured it. After that she decided to treat herself to dinner at the restaurant. The rain hadn't abated and, although she took her big umbrella, she had to put up with the aroma of a damp dog who snored at her feet throughout the meal. She received a warm welcome from Roberto the waiter and his boss and had just finished her *paccheri al pomodoro e basilico*, wonderful, tasty little tubes of pasta in an aromatic tomato and fresh basil sauce, when her heart skipped a beat – momentarily.

Into the restaurant walked a tall, fair-haired man who looked all too familiar, and for a moment her spirits soared but then, a second later, he was followed by a big black dog. Behind him was Simonetta. This had to be Tommaso Montorso, not his twin brother. Alice took a mouthful of red wine to submerge her disappointment and waved across to them.

'Ciao, Simonetta. It's good to see you.'

Simonetta led Tommaso across to Alice's table where Frank jumped to his feet to give the other lab an olfactory greeting. 'It's good to see you too, Alice, but didn't you tell me you were having dinner with my man's brother?' She glanced sideways at Tommaso and gave him a little smile.

'Let me introduce you properly. Alice, this is Tommi. Tommi, this is Alice. I've told you all about her.'

'Ciao, Alice.' He bent forward and shook her hand with his left hand while fending off Frank with the other. Alice was relieved to find that the touch of Tommi's hand didn't produce the same thrill that his brother aroused in her – or at least had done so far. He looked up from the dog. 'And Luca's told me a lot about you.'

'Nice things, I hope.'

'*Very* nice things.' Tommaso gave her a little smile. 'He thinks a lot of you.' Beneath the smile, however, Alice had the impression he was far from happy. Maybe this was because he had told his father about his relationship with Simonetta and all hell had broken loose.

Simonetta repeated her original question. 'No Luca? How come he's stood you up when you had a date arranged?'

Alice realised that this was the opportunity she needed to find out more. Fortunately she was sitting in the corner of the restaurant and the nearby tables were not yet occupied, but she kept her voice down all the same. 'I got a call from him this morning telling me he's had to go off to somewhere down south. Some sort of medical emergency for somebody he knows down there. That's why I'm looking after Frank.'

'An emergency, really?' Simonetta looked as puzzled as Alice had been feeling, but when Alice shot a quick glance at Tommaso's face, she distinctly got the impression that the news hadn't come a surprise to him. Simonetta must have noticed this as well as she turned towards him and put him on the spot. 'Who could that be, Tommi? Somebody you know?'

Tommaso was looking uncomfortable. 'Erm… I'm not sure.' He sounded hesitant but Simonetta wanted more – as did Alice.

'So who do you think it is?' Simonetta glanced sideways at Alice. 'Was it a man or a woman who was having the medical emergency?'

'Luca said it was a woman.'

Simonetta turned back to Tommaso. 'Who is she, Tommi? Is it a friend or a relative or…'

There was a tense hiatus for a second or two before he replied. 'I'm afraid I can't tell you.'

'Can't or won't? Come on, Tommi, you can tell *me*.'

He shook his head. 'I'm sorry, but I promised.' He looked across at Alice. 'But it's not what you think.'

Simonetta had another couple of tries but Tommi either didn't know or he wouldn't say. The two of them finally bade Alice farewell and went off to their own table as her grilled lamb chops and roast potatoes arrived. Alice was vaguely conscious that the meat tasted good, but her mind was far away from food. This latest information only added to her bewilderment, rather than helping to relieve it. The only glimmer of hope in her confusion had been Tommi's words:

'It's not what you think.'

Chapter 24

The weekend passed slowly for Alice. She hadn't found sleep easy overnight, her mind still churning over the possible ramifications of what might be happening in a hospital south of Rome. She had come close to calling Luca to find out what was going on but had given up on the idea. When all was said and done, this was his business and although she had felt herself growing closer to him, their relationship had hardly begun. After all, she reminded herself, she hadn't mentioned a single word to him about any of the handful of embryonic relationships she had had over the years, let alone Maurizio. She could hardly accuse him of doing anything she hadn't done. No doubt he would reveal all when he returned – assuming he did return.

It rained on and off most of Saturday but when she awoke on Sunday morning it had stopped and there were patches of blue sky above. That afternoon, after a long walk with Frank – who was fast developing into a trusted confidant who, while he didn't offer much in the way of advice, was an excellent listener – she sat down for a cup of tea and was about to call her mum for a chat when her phone started ringing. It was Luca, and despite all her uncertainties and fears, she couldn't miss the little leap her heart gave as she saw his caller ID.

'Ciao, Luca, how's things?'

'Okay, thanks. Listen, Alice, I'm really sorry for rushing off like that.' He hesitated briefly. 'It was an emergency. Things here are complicated. I'll tell you all about it when I come back.'

Alice couldn't help giving him a little prompt. 'I saw Tommi and Simonetta on Friday night at the restaurant and he was very mysterious.'

'I promise I'll tell you all about it when I get back. Like I say, it's complicated.'

'Your friend in the hospital, is she seriously ill? Is she going to be all right?' Whatever this woman's relation to Luca, she must have been in a bad way for him to rush off like this.

'Yes, thank God.' She was pleased to hear him sounding more upbeat but she couldn't help wondering whether his delight that his lady friend was getting better might signify a rapprochement between the two of them – whoever she was.

'Oh, good.' What else could she say?

'It's a long sad story and I'll explain when I see you. By the way, that should be some time tomorrow. If you can stand the sight of me, maybe we could have that dinner together at my place…'

'I'd like that, Luca.' And she meant it, although how the evening progressed would depend very much on the explanation he'd give her for his sudden departure.

Monday saw the start of the logging operation headed by Rocco from the sawmill, and a convoy of huge vehicles crawled up the track through the trees to the spot chosen for the start of the operation. Barely an hour later, the unmistakable sound of chainsaws filled the air and Alice walked up to take a look. The clouds had completely cleared by now and the sun was beating down relentlessly although the soft ground had been badly churned up by the heavy trucks. It was still only the beginning of July and Alice could see why rich people from the industrial plains invested in apartments and houses in the Apennines so they could get away from the oppressive heat when high summer arrived. Up here it was hot, but not terribly hot. From her point of view, warm weather meant less discomfort from her leg and she was pleased to find she could walk up the track today without the aid of her stick and almost without any pain, although the deep puddles left over from Saturday night's rain slowed her progress. Or her way she stopped off at Alfonso and Pietro's workshop and found Domenico there. It was his first day.

Domenico, known to all as Mimmo, was the farmhand who had worked for Cesare Montorso for years before finally walking out in the face of his employer's increasingly erratic behaviour. He was a strongly built man in his mid-fifties who already knew Alfonso and Pietro well, and Alice found him up at their workshop, drinking coffee. She accepted a cup of coffee from Pietro in one of the new shiny white mugs she had bought as a present for them and she was rewarded by what looked like coffee without anything unwelcome floating in it. She chatted to the three of them and received an update on what had been going on. As usual, it was Alfonso who did most of the talking.

'We've almost finished building the new chicken run. There are so many foxes in the area we've had to roof the whole thing with wire which has taken some time, but we have twenty laying hens coming next week, so Ines should be able to make all the omelettes and cakes she wants. And four more alpacas are coming on Wednesday.'

Pietro roused himself at the mention of alpacas and was soon giving Alice a detailed account of how the herd was progressing and of his plans for the future. He appeared to have embraced the role of alpaca keeper with enthusiasm. Alice chatted to Mimmo and found him friendly and increasingly communicative after a slow start. As the conversation progressed, he even started talking about what working for the mayor had been like and Alice listened enthralled.

'When I first started he was a whole lot better than he is now. Yes, he could be moody but he wasn't too bad – at least, not with me. Things weren't good at home, though. You know his son Luca went off and left, and then a few years later his wife did the same. I don't blame her. Many were the times I heard him screaming and shouting at her, poor woman.'

'And Tommaso? He's still there.'

'Tommi's vital to the farm and his father's not stupid. He knows that if Tommi were to leave, he'd be in all sorts of trouble, so the two of them coexist – not happily, but they make it work. Anyway, after his wife left, Cesare became ever more aggressive and abusive towards other people, starting with me, and he's been getting steadily worse and worse. There's a limit to the number of times you can be sworn at and insulted. In the end I knew I had to get away and I'm glad I did.' He looked across at Alice. 'He's getting really bad. Something awful's going to happen, I can feel it.'

Around late afternoon Alice got a call from Luca to tell her he was on the autostrada south of Florence and hoped to be back by six or so. She had been thinking about this and she had a suggestion for him.

'I know you said I should come to your house for dinner, but you must be exhausted. The Casa Rosa's closed on a Monday so why don't you come to my place and I'll prepare something?'

He tried to object but he sounded weary and she insisted until he agreed. She took Frank for a quick walk and then went back to her place to prepare dinner, stopping off at the minimarket to buy some ham and salami as well as fresh strawberries and raspberries and a tub of ice cream. As it was still very warm, she decided to make a Caesar salad, which could be prepared in advance so she would be able to devote herself to hearing Luca's story without distractions. What he had to tell her remained to be discovered, but she was feeling increasingly nervous as the minutes went by. What if he was coming to tell her he had another woman?

It was a quarter to seven when he finally appeared, apologising for the delay. There was an awkward hiatus at the door before he gave her a little peck on the lips and bent down to return his dog's enthusiastic greeting. For a moment Alice almost felt jealous of Frank and she wondered if this presaged some change in the way Luca felt about her. As he stroked the happy Labrador he looked up and explained that there had been a big accident on the motorway which had held him up. Irrespective of what he had come here to tell her, Alice was just relieved that he hadn't been involved in it. She poured him a glass of cold white wine and watched him sit down on the sofa with his happy dog climbing all over him. She sat down opposite him and waited to hear his story. She didn't have long to wait.

'Like I say, I'm so sorry I had to rush off like that but it was an emergency.' She saw him take a big mouthful of wine – Dutch courage, maybe? 'I should have told you before but, you see, Tommi and I have been sharing a big secret for years.'

Alice gave him a puzzled look. 'You and Tommi?'

'Yes, you see, it's our mother. She lives in Terracina now, but it's a closely guarded secret. After she left home eight years ago she came south to where I was working and I found her a place to live and she's made a new life for herself. She's found herself a job in a dairy making mozzarella and I wouldn't mind betting that she'll be running the place before too long. I know my father and I'm convinced that if he ever found out where she's living he'd be down there like a shot, and who knows what might happen? She's still terrified of him and she never ever wants to see him again. She made Tommi and me promise to keep her whereabouts a secret. Nobody's supposed to know, so that's why I couldn't tell you before.'

The fog in Alice's brain was rapidly dispersing. His mother! 'And how is she now? Why was she taken to hospital?'

'Acute appendicitis. She'd been having stomach pains for a while and things suddenly took a turn for the worse on Friday. They rushed her in and she had an emergency operation that same afternoon. The medics say the appendix was badly swollen and they just got to it in time before it perforated. The good news is that she's fine now and should be up and about in a day or two. I've come back, and Tommi's on his way down to see her.' He looked up from the dog. 'I gather Simonetta has broken the news of their relationship to the baron and he's okay with it. Well, Tommi did the same with our father at the weekend and, no surprise, he went ballistic. Tommi's only too pleased to get away from him, but he's worried for the animals. I said I'd go round tomorrow to check that the cows are being milked and the chickens fed.'

'You're going to your father's farm?' Alice looked at him apprehensively. 'Aren't you afraid he might do something stupid?'

'Well, he isn't going to assault me, that's for sure. He's getting old now and he knows I'm prepared to stand up for myself.' He produced a little smile for Alice's benefit. 'He'll probably give me an earful but I couldn't care less. I told Tommi I'd go over in the morning so hopefully at that time of day my father will be at the town hall and I'll have the place to myself.'

Then, to Alice's delight, he abandoned the Labrador, jumped to his feet and stretched out his hands towards her. 'Anyway, it's wonderful to see you again. I've missed you so much over these past few days and I've been thinking about you a lot.'

Alice jumped up as well and went over to catch hold of his hands. 'And I've been thinking about you too. A lot.' He pulled her towards him and kissed her for so long that her legs almost gave way beneath her, but his arms stopped her from falling.

Finally she pulled back and gazed up into his eyes. 'That was rather nice, Signor Montorso.'

'Rather nice?' He beamed back at her. 'You English, you love understatement, don't you? That was without doubt the most amazing kiss I've ever had.'

She grinned back at him as she kissed him softly on the lips. 'I couldn't have put it better myself. Now, if you're hungry, there's food in the fridge, unless you had any other ideas?'

He had other ideas.

And that was rather nice, too.

Chapter 25

Next morning Alice woke with a broad smile on her face and, feeling movement beside her, rolled over and immediately received a blast of unsavoury Labrador breath, followed by the feel of a long tongue attempting to lick her face.

'Frank! You were told to stay in the living room.' She felt a movement on the other side of her and turned her head to see Luca smiling at her over her bare shoulder.

'At least he didn't bother us in the night, but I think he's telling me he wants his early morning walk.' He kissed her tenderly on the earlobe and she felt a little shiver run through her. 'By the way, have I told you that last night was, as you English would put it, rather nice?'

'Last night was amazing.' She twisted round and kissed him back while doing her best to dissuade the Labrador from climbing up to join them on the bed. Finally, as she felt heavy paws land on the bed, she gave in to the inevitable and pulled back from Luca and adopted a stern tone. 'Frank, get off! And, Luca, why don't you go and take your dog for a walk before he climbs in here with us? While you do that, I'll sort out some breakfast.'

By the time Luca came back she had prepared fresh coffee, toast and, unsure what he liked for breakfast, she had made a ham omelette as well, calculating that if he didn't eat it she could have it cold for lunch. As it turned out he ate everything.

At half past eight she left him and his dog and went up to the castle where she met Simonetta who was looking concerned.

'Ciao, Alice, did Luca get back safely?' Something on Alice's face must have given her away and Simonetta gave her a grin. 'Of course he did. Did he tell you why he had to go off and why Tommi's gone down south now? Tommi revealed the big mystery to me before he left. So much for you fearing Luca had another woman down there.'

Alice nodded. 'I shouldn't have doubted him. And as for their mother, how can a man behave so terribly towards his wife and his children? Little wonder she ran off and never wants to see him again.'

'Absolutely. Is Luca coming here to the castle today? There's a letter and a long questionnaire from the *Belle Arti* that needs to be completed.'

'I'm not sure.' Alice went on to tell her where Luca was spending the morning and Simonetta shook her head uncertainly.

'I hope he's all right. Tommi said his father's totally lost it. He was shouting and screaming and hurling threats at everybody from our family to Tommi and Luca, and even at the population of Varaldo for "betraying" him.' She lowered her voice apprehensively. 'Tommi even took the shotgun and hid it, just in case.'

Alice was horrified. 'Thank God for that. The thought of what a bitter, unstable man could do with a shotgun in a townful of people doesn't bear thinking about.' She pulled out her phone. 'I'd better call Luca and warn him his father's flipped.' She tried three times but each time she just got the *Unable to Connect* message. Simonetta wasn't surprised.

'The signal's terrible on the other side of the valley. I often can't get through to Tommi unless he's up on top of one of the hills.' She looked at her watch. 'I know, let's go over and look for him. I'll give Emilia a call and see if we can take the horses out. It would be good to get some fresh air.'

Half an hour later they were on horseback. Simonetta led the way up the track so they could circle Montorso land. That way they could look down onto the farm without trespassing and risk increasing the fury of the deranged mayor. As the horses picked their way up the hillside, Alice gave Simonetta an edited version of the previous evening and night and received a beaming smile in response.

'You see, I told you that you were worrying about nothing. I'm so happy for you, for you both. Tommi's been worried about Luca for ages. He's always working – or visiting their mother. Hopefully with your influence he'll be able to relax and lead a more normal life.'

'I suppose that'll partly depend on what happens to his father. He can't go on like this.' As she spoke, Alice began to hear the sound of a powerful diesel engine in the distance and as they rounded a curve in the track she spotted a red flash through the trees. A few yards further on this was revealed as a tractor and it was clear that it was ploughing one of the steeper fields above the farm. Alice had done her fair share of tractor driving and ploughing in her younger days and she knew how important it was to keep straight lines and avoid missing patches of ground. To her expert eye, it was clear that this particular tractor driver was either inexperienced, drunk or there was something seriously wrong with his concentration. She exchanged glances with Simonetta.

'If that's Luca up there, he's badly out of practice. If it's his father, I have a feeling his mind's not on the job. Talk about erratic…'

Simonetta stood up in the stirrups and peered across the hillside that sloped gently at first and then dropped away sharply. 'Let's go over and take a closer look. At least if it is the mayor and he starts getting abusive, our horses can easily outrun a tractor on this kind of terrain.'

Pressing the horses into a trot, they made their way up the path until they reached the edge of the field where they could clearly see the tractor ploughing its way up the frighteningly steep part of the slope less than a hundred yards away on the far side. The earth was still damp from the weekend's rain and the rich brown of the furrows stood out against the green of the unturned ground. It was immediately clear that it wasn't Luca at the wheel. Even from this distance they could make out the unmistakable red-faced figure of Cesare Montorso. They reined in while they decided on their next move and Alice studied the ploughed field critically.

'He's only done about a quarter of the field. I would think it's going to take him at least a couple of hours to do the whole thing, so we've probably got time to turn round and go back down to the farmhouse to find Luca.'

Simonetta nodded in agreement. 'I imagine Luca's worked out for himself by now that his father's out on the tractor so I expect he's down there looking after the livestock. Come on, let's go.'

No sooner had she spoken however, than they heard a shout. The mayor had seen them and he was waving his arms at them, no doubt telling them to get off his land even though technically they were on the track rather than his field.

'Let's get out of here.' As Simonetta pulled on the reins and turned her horse back downhill, Alice saw the mayor spin the wheel and turn the tractor towards them, still gesticulating wildly. She stared in disbelief. It was a suicidal manoeuvre on a slope like this, but the man clearly wasn't thinking straight. She looked on in horror as the tractor turned side on to the slope and as it did so, even all the tractor's weight was unable to cope with the gradient, and the whole thing slowly started to slide sideways on the damp ground until it gradually began to topple inexorably over onto its side. By this time the mayor must have realised his mistake and Alice saw him desperately fighting to turn back up the slope but the damage had been done. The massive machine tipped over, the engine racing as the huge wheels lost all grip on the ground, and Alice lost sight of the driver. The weight of the tractor caused it to slide on its side for several more yards before it came to rest, precariously poised at the top of the steepest part of the hillside, apparently only held in place by a thread.

'Jesus!' Alice turned towards Simonetta who was already trotting down the track, oblivious to what had just happened. 'Simonetta! Come back!'

Alice waited to see her friend acknowledge her cry and then spurred Horace across the field towards the tractor. Leaping off him onto the soft ground she immediately found herself sprawled on her face as her bad leg dug in and she lost her footing. Fortunately she was still holding the reins and she was able to use them to help pull herself to her feet as Horace stood there placidly and helped himself to mouthfuls of grass. Abandoning the reins, she straightened up, did her best to wipe the worst of the mud and earth from her hands and face, and made her way cautiously over to the tractor.

Seen close up it was in an even more precarious position than had first appeared. The whole of the engine, driver's seat and steering wheel were hanging in mid-air over a slope that was brutally steep, while the engine revved out of control and the wheels continued to spin vainly, making the ground around it tremble. Gingerly she made her way around until she could reach up to switch off the engine, acutely conscious as she did so that six or seven tons of metal were poised precariously above her. In the sudden silence she stepped back and looked around, searching for any sign of the mayor. At first she saw nothing, but then a faint movement not far from her feet caught her eye and she realised she had found him.

It was clear that he had been pushed down the hill by the weight of the sliding tractor and he was coated from head to foot in thick, viscous mud that had virtually concealed him from her at first glance. He was lying directly beneath the main body of the tractor and only his upper body, head and shoulders were visible. His legs were completely hidden beneath one of the huge wheels. As she looked down at him his eyes opened and he reached up towards her, struggling to articulate.

'I can't feel my legs.' He gave no sign of recognition and in spite of everything she felt a sudden wave of sympathy for him. She knew only too well what it felt like to be in this position. She sat down awkwardly beside him –

kneeling was something she found almost impossible since the accident – and looked at him, doing her best not to let her mind dwell on the very real risk of the whole thing tipping over on top of both of them. Cesare Montorso was now looking a far cry from the irascible despot she had seen on stage at the town hall. She reached across and gently wiped the mud from his face.

'Try not to worry. We'll get you out of it.'

His eyes didn't reopen but there was the faintest movement of his face muscles that indicated he had heard. She sat there for a minute or two before slowly and carefully sliding backwards, away from the tractor. With difficulty she scrambled awkwardly to her feet, now plastered with almost as much mud as the mayor. She was just emerging around the front of the tractor when Simonetta appeared, holding both horses by the reins.

'How is he?'

'It's not good.' Alice outlined the situation to her. 'He's trapped under the weight of the tractor and I've no idea how bad his injuries are but my main fear is that the whole thing might roll over on top of him at any moment. If it does, it'll crush him and then slide over the edge and drag him down the hill.' She didn't need to spell out what the result would be if that happened.

Simonetta had her phone in her hand but she was snorting in frustration. 'It's no good. There's no signal. They must have a landline in the farmhouse. One of us had better get down there to call the emergency services.'

Alice made a quick decision. 'You go. You know your way around better than I do. I'll stay here with him. See if you can find Luca while you're down there.'

'Are you sure you're going to be all right on your own?' Simonetta sounded hesitant.

Alice smiled up at her with a confidence she didn't feel. 'I'll be fine. I'll stay with him until you get back with reinforcements.'

'Just you be careful. That tractor looks as if it could topple over at any moment.' Simonetta climbed back onto her horse and cantered off across the hillside. Horace just stood there unperturbed, helping himself to more of the rough grass, oblivious to the drama taking place around him.

Alice watched Simonetta disappear down the track for a few moments before taking a deep breath and turning back towards the injured man. Like it or lump it, she knew what she had to do. She slogged back through the mud to where the stricken man lay and allowed herself to slump back onto the ground alongside him. The brooding presence of the huge machine balanced above her was intimidating but she steeled herself and did her best to ignore it. The mayor's outstretched arm was lying close by her so she caught hold of his hand and gave it a little squeeze.

'Help's on its way. You'll be okay.'

At first there was no response from him but after a full minute she saw his eyes open. They were bloodshot and wracked with pain and her heart went out to him. The resemblance to his two sons was all too evident and she felt tears of pity spring to the corners of her eyes, but she wiped them away with the back of her free hand. Bursting into tears wouldn't help anybody.

'You're the Varaldo girl, aren't you? You work for them?' His voice was little more than a croak, but she was heartened to hear him making sense.

'Yes, I'm Alice. Simonetta has gone off to get help and Luca will be here soon. We'll get you out of this. Try to conserve your strength until the medics arrive.'

'Luca's here?' The disbelief in his tone said it all. 'He won't help me. He hates me.'

As she looked down at him, Alice's mind went back to the awful moment four years earlier when she had woken to find herself buried beneath a metre of snow, unable to move without sending excruciating stabs of pain throughout her whole body. Even when her rescuers had arrived, she had had to lie there for almost an hour while they laboured to dig her out. A friendly paramedic called Stefano had crouched there with her the whole time, holding her hand and keeping her talking. They had talked about everything from skiing to horse riding, and when he had visited her in hospital a few days later he had told her that in these situations it was vital to keep the victim awake if possible, so she did her best to do the same with Luca's father.

'Luca doesn't hate you. He's your son. You'll see.'

'He hates me. So does Tommaso. They both hate me. They all hate me.' There was no defiance or aggression in his voice now, just resignation.

'Of course they don't hate you.' Even she could hear how hollow her words sounded but she knew she had to make the effort.

'Everybody hates me, everybody's against me.' He was sounding less and less intelligible, his speech slurring as his eyes closed again and Alice jumped in to keep him talking.

'I don't hate you. If I hated you, why would I be here alongside you? Why would Simonetta be riding down the hill like a mad thing to get help if she hated you?'

To her surprise, his eyes opened once more. 'Why *are* you here?' There was scepticism in his voice. 'You hate me, they all hate me...'

'Like I've been telling you, I don't hate you. Besides, I know what you're going through.'

'You do? Of course you don't.' There was a faint trace of his former arrogance in his scathing tone and Alice felt herself bristle.

'See this?' She reached down with her free hand and pulled up the left leg of her breeches, revealing her prosthetic limb. 'Now do you believe me?'

She went on to tell him what had happened, making sure to keep pushing him to respond to what she was saying. She told him everything, from the despair and the agony to the hope and relief, and then to the bleak realisation that she would be disabled for life. 'But I'm still here and I'm loving life again.' Seeing his eyes begin to close, she searched desperately for something to say to stimulate him and produced a spontaneous comment that surprised even her as it leapt to her lips. 'And if you don't believe me, ask your son. I know Luca well now. In fact, I'm in love with him.' Although she was honest enough to admit that her feelings for Luca had been strengthening day by day ever since she had first set eyes on him, this was the first time she had used the 'L' word to anybody, even herself.

It worked. His eyes opened once more. 'Luca? Did you say Luca? You're in love with Luca?'

Alice instinctively glanced over her shoulder in case Luca might have crept up and overheard, but she was still alone on the hillside with the critically injured man. For now all that mattered was to keep him talking so she nodded. 'Yes. I think he's a wonderful man.'

'You do…?'

His voice tailed off and Alice was desperately searching for something else to say to keep the stricken man from losing consciousness when she heard the sound of a vehicle approaching. She squeezed his hand again and leant closer to him.

'Can you hear that? Help's arrived. I'm just going to show them where we are and then I'll be back. Can you hear me? I said I'll be back.'

There might have been a response but it was hard to tell. Beneath the coating of mud, the mayor was as white as a sheet and Alice had a feeling he was probably losing a lot of blood. The sooner they got him out of there the better. She wriggled backwards until she could pull herself to her feet and make her way around the side of the tractor. As she came out from beneath the overhang she felt an acute sense of relief, immediately tempered by the knowledge that there was still a human being under there. She emerged to see the mayor's battered Toyota pickup being driven down the field towards her. At the wheel was Luca. He skidded to a halt and jumped out. As he did so, Alice spotted a big black shape on the passenger seat, but Luca wisely left Frank in the vehicle for now. He came running across and stopped in front of her.

'Are you all right? I can hardly see you for mud.'

She did her best to explain the situation but Luca was already on his way around to see for himself and as he disappeared from sight beneath the body of the tractor she had a sudden shiver of fear at what might happen. If it toppled over it would crush both men and, bizarrely, this frightened her more than if she had been under there herself. She squelched around after Luca and found him on his knees by his father's side, talking to him. It was impossible to hear what he was saying or to make out any response from his father but she decided to give them some space and left them to it.

As her eyes landed on the pickup truck an idea occurred to her and she hurried across to it. She searched through the chaotic jumble in the back of the truck that had no doubt been thrown about as Luca had charged up the hill until she found what she was looking for: a coil of rope. Grabbing it, she went around to the driver's door and climbed in, fending off the joyful greeting of the Labrador as she did so. The key was still in the ignition and she started the engine. Unlike her car, this wasn't an automatic and she had to struggle to operate the clutch. It wasn't easy but she managed it. It was already in the low ratio gearbox and she was reassured to find that the tyres gripped well and she could reverse back up the field without too much trouble. When she was directly above the overturned tractor she inched back down towards it until she was barely a few metres from it.

Leaving the dog where he was, she picked up the rope and jumped out again. Treading as delicately as she could, she looped the rope around one of the exposed axles of the tractor and ran it back to the front of the pickup. She had just finished fastening it when she heard Luca's voice behind her.

'Good thinking.' She saw his eyes flick to her bad leg. 'Do you want me to reverse it up?'

'Please. I doubt if the pickup will be powerful enough to pull the tractor upright but at least it should help to keep it from toppling further down the slope.' She stepped back and watched as he gradually reversed back up the slope until the rope tightened. He had just set the brake and switched off the engine, and was climbing back out again when a flashing blue light indicated the arrival of a Land Rover in red fire brigade livery.

After that, things happened remarkably quickly. After a brief conversation with the fire chief, the red Land Rover was manoeuvred into position alongside the pickup and also attached to the upper part of the underside of the tractor with a hefty rope. Both vehicles then reversed cautiously up the slope and their joint efforts resulted in the tractor slowly being pulled until it toppled back upright and away from the injured man. By this time another 4x4, this one containing two paramedics, had arrived and they took charge of the victim. All this excitement was watched with disinterest by Horace the horse who just kept on munching on the grass.

Alice suddenly felt very weary and unexpectedly cold so she climbed into the pickup and slumped onto the passenger seat to the delight of the Labrador, who immediately climbed onto her lap. She hugged him willingly and within seconds he was as muddy as she was but neither of them minded. She let her eyes close and drifted into a trance-like state until she was roused by the sound of the driver's door and she opened her eyes to see Luca climb in.

'Frank, get off! You'll squash Alice.'

'No, leave him, Luca, he's heavy but he's lovely and warm. I got very cold all of a sudden.' She managed a little smile. 'It's just shock and a lot of not so pleasant memories, but I'll be fine. How's your dad?'

'Not good. His legs are crushed and he's lost an awful lot of blood, but by some miracle they think he's going to be okay.' He caught her eye for a moment. 'Of course you know only too well what he's going through. They've filled him full of painkillers and the plan is to get him onto a stretcher and take him up to the top of the field where it's flat enough for the air ambulance to pick him up and fly him to hospital in Parma.' His brow furrowed in concern. 'Are you sure you're all right?'

'I'm fine. Like I say, it's just been a bit of shock.'

'I was able to talk to my father for a little while before the medics got to him.' There was now a different, more quizzical expression on his face and Alice felt the colour rush to her cheeks as she had a premonition of what was to come next. She wasn't wrong.

'He told me you said you're in love with me. Is that true?'

She reached over and caught hold of his forearm. 'I'm sorry, I was trying to keep your father talking and it was the first thing that came into my head.'

'So you didn't mean it?'

Realising she risked digging herself into a hole, she avoided answering the question. 'I'm sorry, it just sprang to mind. It was all a bit stressful down there, with that tractor hanging over my head. I wasn't thinking straight.'

'So you didn't mean it?' He wasn't giving up so she threw caution to the wind.

'I didn't say that.'

'So you did mean it?'

She knew when she was beaten. 'Yes, I did.' She didn't know what else to say.

His smile broadened. 'Well, that, Miss Sterling, is definitely rather nice.'

Chapter 26

The next six months flew by. Planning permission for work on the castle to begin was granted remarkably quickly and all the way through the autumn a procession of tradesmen's vans and trucks filled the courtyard. A full modernisation programme was set in train and by the time the first hard frosts of winter arrived, the brand new radiators in Alice's office kept her cosy and warm. Regular visits from Luca also did a lot to keep her cosy and warm. And very happy.

When Christmas came around, they arranged that he would go south to visit his mother but then would return between Christmas and New Year so that he and Alice could spend the festivities together. She took advantage of his absence to go back to England and see her own folks. Her father came to collect her from the station in the pickup truck and she was mildly surprised to find that when they got back to the farm, he didn't immediately drive up to the house. Instead, he turned into the high field and drove right to the top, the four-wheel drive making light work of the frozen rutted ground. He pulled up by the top gate and indicated that she should get out with him. She did as instructed and he led her over to the gate and pointed.

'Look what we've got now!'

There, looking perfectly at home, were a dozen or so alpacas. She turned towards him and gave him a big smile.

'What happened to the ostriches?'

He grinned back at her. 'I was contacted by a guy in Somerset who wanted to start ostrich farming and he made me an offer. I was so glad to get rid of the things, I almost bit his hand off, which coincidentally is what those damn birds kept trying to do to me and the guys. You can't beat alpacas – placid, hardy, good-natured. How's your herd?'

'Thirty-six now and more on the way. We've been getting the local schoolchildren along to take them for walks and they all seem to love it – and by that I mean the kids *and* the animals. We'll start advertising properly when the castle opens to the public.'

'When's that going to be?'

'Easter, if all goes well.'

'And how's it all going at the moment?'

On the way down to the house she gave him more detail of the remedial works being undertaken as well as the various changes imposed by the planners in order for them to be able to open to the public. Any further discussion of practical matters was interrupted when they got home and her mother came running out of the front door, gave her a warm hug and dragged her inside. The Aga in the kitchen was pumping out the heat and there was a wonderful smell of roasting food in the air. Pushing Alice into a chair, her mum set about making tea and the 'inquisition' began. Although she had given most of the news to her mum during their regular phone conversations over the past few months, this didn't come as a surprise.

'Tell me about Luca. Is everything still all right between the two of you?'

Alice answered honestly. 'Everything's wonderful. Things really couldn't be better.'

'I'm so pleased for you. When are we going to meet him?'

'As you can imagine, he and I are up to our eyes at the moment with all the work at the castle but we're planning the grand opening at Easter, and you really have to come over for that, if you can't come over before.' She glanced across at her father. 'Do you think you could get away for a few days?'

She was delighted to see him nod. 'We've been talking about a holiday for a while, and now that I've got Stan trained up and working well, I'm sure I should be able to get away at least for a few days or maybe even a week.'

Alice smiled back at him. She knew that farming was a full-time job, and getting time off one of the biggest problems for anybody in the business. Animals still needed to be fed, crops still needed to be planted, nurtured and harvested, and there were all the hundreds of other things that needed to be done to keep a farm working happily.

'That sounds wonderful. I know Luca's looking forward to meeting you.'

'What about his parents?' There was a more serious look on her mother's face now. 'How's the father? Did you say he might be able to walk again after all?'

'He's lost one leg up to the thigh and he's had a new knee and reconstructive surgery on the other one, but from what I hear, he's already having physio and beginning to move around on it. He'll never be *fully* mobile again but, if you'd seen what happened, you'd realise just how lucky he's been.'

'Is he still the mayor?'

Alice shook her head. 'No, after everything that happened, he resigned his position and his place has been taken by his one time arch-enemy, Giorgio from the local restaurant.'

'And how about his other problems...? Is he still shouting and screaming at people?'

'No, it's been amazing. Luca and Tommi say their father's calmed down completely as a result of the new drugs he's now on. He's been diagnosed with something called IED, Intermittent Explosive Disorder, which had plagued him – and those around him – all his life.'

'And how are things between the two boys and their father? From what you've told me they had a terrible time growing up.'

Alice nodded. 'I can only imagine how grim it must have been. Tommi has now taken over running the farm and I think he and his dad have pretty much buried the hatchet. Tommi knows full well that his father was a sick man and that he didn't mean to mistreat them. It was just what was going on inside his head. Now that that's been fixed he says his father's a changed man.'

'And what about Luca? After all, he spent ten years or more without ever seeing or speaking to his dad, didn't you say? Do you think he understands and can forgive?'

'He definitely understands that it was an illness and although they don't see much of each other yet, I have a feeling things will gradually work out between them.'

'And the mother?'

'She's moved on. She's met a guy where she now lives and they're getting married in the new year. She still sees a lot of the boys but I don't think she'll ever be able to forgive and forget as far as her husband's concerned.'

'Well, at least it sounds as though she's happy now.'

Dinner was roast beef with all the trimmings. Her mum had prepared roast potatoes, cauliflower cheese, Yorkshire pudding and, inevitably, sprouts. Alice had never been a great fan of sprouts but she made an effort and thoroughly enjoyed the meal. By the time she had put away some of her mum's home-made bread and butter pudding with custard and clotted cream, she felt absolutely stuffed and happy to be home.

If she had thought the questioning was over, she was to be disappointed. While her dad filled all of their glasses with some good claret, her mum brought the conversation back to Varaldo again.

'And what about the family at the castle? I think it's wonderful that you and Simonetta have ended up with a twin each. Are things working out well for her and Tommi?'

'Things are working out very well. He proposed to her only a few days ago and they're planning to get married next summer. And, as if that wasn't enough, her brother, Achille, is also now engaged to his beloved Silvia, so that means there'll be two weddings coming up next year.'

Her mother looked up from the remains of her pudding and gave her an inquisitive smile. 'Or maybe even three…?'

Alice smiled back. 'Who knows?'

Her father tactfully changed the subject and soon he and Alice were discussing the merits of dairy as compared to beef cattle and technical questions like the gestation period of the alpaca.

—

On Christmas Eve, Alice was invited over to the Dower House for lunch with Fenella and Ronald. Lord F-C had insisted on driving over in person to collect her. He turned up in his beloved 1927 Rolls Royce that Fenella had told Alice he only used for very, very special occasions. Alice was flattered and most impressed, and as she admired it on the drive back, she told him the story of the Mercedes that Luca had discovered at the castle.

'It was sold at auction last month for just over half a million euros. I shudder to think how much your Rolls Royce must be worth.'

He shot her a little grin as he squeezed the massive old car slowly past an elderly lady taking her pair of sausage dogs for a walk along the lane. 'That's what my accountant keeps asking me, but as long as I'm alive, this car stays in the family.'

Fenella greeted Alice with hugs and kisses and led her into the sitting room where Alice received a boisterous and noisy greeting from Gladys the poodle. There was a bottle of champagne on ice in a bucket and soon Ronald was toasting Alice's return to Devon. For her part, she had a toast of her own to propose. She held up her glass and beamed at both of them.

'I owe you both a massive thank you. If it hadn't been for your kindness, none of the wonderful things that have happened to me over the past year would have happened. I'm indebted to you both. I just hope I can repay some of your kindness. Cheers.'

Fenella smiled back at her, sipped her wine, and cut to the chase. 'So, Luca? Tell me all about him.'

Although Alice had had a chance to refine her story over the past twenty-four hours with her mum, she still felt her cheeks flush a little at the thought of him. 'He's lovely.' She told them more about him, his job, Frank the dog and how much she loved him. Over the past months she had regularly phoned Fenella to stay in touch and to update her on developments at the castle, but she was unsurprised to find that Fenella was thinking along very similar lines to her mother.

'Are we going to hear wedding bells one of these days?'

Alice blushed again. 'I honestly don't know.'

'Have you discussed it with him?'

'Not really. When Tommi asked Simonetta to marry him just the other day I thought for a moment Luca might be going to say something, but he didn't. The thing is, even in the early stages of our relationship he's always been a bit reticent.'

'Do you think he loves you as much as you do?'

'I hope so. I certainly love him to bits.'

'So if he asked you, you'd say yes?'

'Like a shot.'

'Which means you'd be happy to settle permanently in Italy?'

'I'm already settled in Italy. I love the place. Whether things work out between me and Luca or not, I love my job, love Varaldo and I'm perfectly happy. I'm not going anywhere.'

'I'm so happy for you.' Fenella caught her eye. 'If Luca's taking his time, why don't *you* ask *him* to marry you?' Fenella wasn't giving up easily.

Ronald, who had been studiously staying out of this conversation tut-tutted. 'Goodness me, Fen, give the girl a chance. It'll all work out. Alice, Fen and I've been talking about taking a trip to Italy one of these days. Do you think we could come and see you?'

'I would love for you to come and see me. Come whenever you like. I'm still in my tiny flat for now, but there's a super little hotel in the village where you could stay and the food is excellent. Come when you can but please consider yourselves invited as honoured guests to the party we're going to have at Easter when the castle officially opens to the public.'

Chapter 27

Saturday April the twelfth was a very special day.

At six o'clock in the evening the newly restored draw-bridge was lowered over the now rubbish-free moat, the gleaming portcullis on its new chains hauled up, and the castle was finally open to the public for the very first time. A steady stream of specially invited guests began to arrive and make their way inside. Alice stood to greet them as they passed through the reception area by the main gate and she was delighted to see many familiar faces. As well as a number of locals ranging from Giorgio and Leo from the restaurant to Tonino from the minimarket, there were other guests from further afield, among them *Architetto* Bolognese and his wife, Rocco from the sawmill with his family, and a delegation from the *Belle Arti* who had scrutinised the conversion work every step of the way.

Newly appointed staff members directed the guests up to the first floor where the official opening reception was to take place, and at six thirty Alice took one last nervous glance in the full-length mirror outside her office and hurried upstairs to join the assembled throng. The bar set up in the main living room was dispensing drinks to the guests while half a dozen staff members passed around the room carrying trays of appetisers.

The furniture had been moved so as to allow space for everybody to mingle and Alice spotted her mum and dad over by the fireplace chatting to the baroness with the help of Simonetta who had surprised Alice over the winter by demonstrating an unexpectedly good command of the English language. Alongside them were Fenella and Ronald, who had been only too happy to accept Alice's invitation to come over for the occasion. Lord F–C himself was obviously having a fine time practising the Italian he had learned forty years earlier.

Further along was Achille with Silvia, now his fiancée, who was looking charming, if a bit overwhelmed to be on the arm of the future baron. The baron himself was deep in conversation with the head of the *Belle Arti* and Alice had little doubt that the topic of discussion was likely to be the new museum of the Varaldo family, which was the baron's pride and joy.

As she stood there, she felt a touch against her good leg and glanced down to see a happy dog looking up at her, tail wagging. As she bent down to ruffle his ears, she felt another touch, this time to her bare shoulder, and she looked up to see a familiar and welcome face. She reached up and kissed him on the cheek.

'*Ciao, bello.*' And he was looking *bello* in an immaculate dark grey suit.

'*Ciao, bella.*' He was looking tense and her heart went out to him. It was a big moment for all of them. She saw his eyes flick across towards the door. 'He's arrived. Tommi's down in the courtyard with him. They'll be on their way up in the lift in a minute or so.'

'Okay, I'll go and spread the word.' She gave him an affectionate smile. 'By the way, I like the suit. Very smart.'

'Well, I love the dress. You look gorgeous.'

She glanced down to where her prosthetic leg was on display for the very first time and felt that same shiver of uncertainty that had dogged her ever since he had persuaded her to go out and buy the dress. Reluctantly she had heeded his advice to embrace what had happened to her, but it was taking time to adapt after years of denial.

'You sure?'

In reply he smiled and kissed her again, very softly, on the lips. 'I said gorgeous and I meant gorgeous.'

Reassured, she headed across to Simonetta. 'Luca's just told me they're on their way up.'

Excusing herself to the others, Simonetta set down her glass and went across to tell her father. Alice stood with her parents and Fenella and Ronald while Simonetta's grandmother went over to join the baron as well. Silvia, still looking a bit overwhelmed, appeared at Alice's side as Achille joined the reception party by the doors of the newly installed lift. Alice gave her a supportive smile and caught hold of her hand.

'You look as nervous as I feel. What's it like being seen by everybody as the future Baroness Varaldo?'

'Absolutely terrifying.' Silvia gave Alice's hand a squeeze. 'I'm so pleased for you, Alice. You're so brave.' Her eyes flitted downwards for a second. 'You look wonderful in that dress.'

Alice was about to return the compliment when the lift door hissed open and the hum of conversation in the room dropped. In the ensuing silence Tommi emerged from the lift, pushing the wheelchair out and into the room. As he did so, the baron stepped forward and inclined his head formally in greeting.

'Signor Montorso, welcome to Varaldo Castle.'

The figure in the wheelchair stretched out his hand and returned the greeting, his voice stronger than his shrunken, pallid features would have suggested.

'Thank you for inviting me here, *Barone*. I'm sorry it's taken us so long to come to this point.' He held out his hand towards the baroness. 'It's a pleasure to meet you, Signora Beatrice, and of course I know your granddaughter well by now.'

The old lady took his hand in both of hers and shook it formally. 'You can't imagine how happy I am that the day has finally arrived when our two families can meet in friendship.'

Cesare Montorso insisted on lifting himself unaided from the wheelchair and onto his crutches. Alice couldn't help comparing how he was now, both physically and mentally, to how he had been when she had first met him. As for his crushed legs, he would never walk properly again but she was pleased to see his determination to overcome his disability as much as he could. Somehow, this made her decision to bare her prosthetic leg and be damned so much easier in comparison.

It was heart-breaking that it had taken such a catastrophic accident so similar to her own to bring him the medical care his brain needed and the resulting improvement in his mental health. What they were seeing now was a changed man in so many ways.

As Cesare Montorso and the baron started to converse, Alice felt her mother's hand on her arm and her voice at her ear, sounding unusually emotional.

'You can't imagine how happy your father and I are for you, Alice. I'm not just talking about all this, your job, or even about Luca, but about how you've regained your self-confidence.' She pointed downwards with her free hand. 'I almost burst into tears when I saw you appear in this dress. You look so beautiful…' There was a catch in her voice and Alice leapt in before her mother managed to make both of them cry.

'I couldn't have done it without the support of the two of you over the past few years.'

'And of course you've been helped by somebody else.' A twinkle now appeared in her mother's eye and Alice gave a surreptitious sigh of relief that the crisis had been averted. Her mum reached out and caught hold of her left hand. 'Show me the ring again, would you? It's lovely. I'm so glad he finally asked you. How did he do it?'

'Yesterday morning we rode to a very beautiful place called the Blue Lake and he asked me there.' She could feel the tears threatening to spring to her eyes again at the memory of the moment. 'And I couldn't be happier.'

'I'm delighted for you. You couldn't have done better.'

Alice leant across and gave her mum a kiss on the cheek.

'That's the way I feel, too.'

At that moment she felt a hand land on her shoulder and she glanced up to find Luca there. 'We've just been talking about you.' She was still speaking English so she deliberately spoke slowly, although he, like Simonetta, had surprised her with his ability to speak her language.

'Good things, I hope.'

'Very good things.'

He smiled at her and leant forward to kiss her softly on the forehead.

'Well, that's rather nice.'

Acknowledgements

With warmest thanks to Emily Bedford, my editor, and all the other lovely people at Canelo who do such a wonderful job.